HIGHER SPECIMEN QUESTION PAPER

FOR OFFICIAL USE

Total
Section B

X012/301

NATIONAL
QUALIFICATIONS

Time: 2 hours 30 minutes

CHEMISTRY
HIGHER
Specimen Question Paper

Fill in these boxes and read what is printed below.

Full name of centre

Town

Forename(s)

Surname

Date of birth
Day Month Year

Scottish candidate number

Number of seat

Reference may be made to the Chemistry Higher and Advanced Higher Data Booklet (1999 edition).

SECTION A—Questions 1–40

Instructions for completion of **Section A** are given on page two.

SECTION B

1   All questions should be attempted.

2   The questions may be answered in any order but all answers are to be written in the spaces provided in this answer book, and must be written clearly and legibly in ink.

3   Rough work, if any should be necessary, should be written in this book and then scored through when the fair copy has been written.

4   Additional space for answers and rough work will be found at the end of the book. If further space is required, supplementary sheets may be obtained from the invigilator and should be inserted inside the **front** cover of this book.

5   The size of the space provided for an answer should not be taken as an indication of how much to write. It is not necessary to use all the space.

6   Before leaving the examination room you must give this book to the invigilator. If you do not, you may lose all the marks for this paper.

SCOTTISH
QUALIFICATIONS
AUTHORITY
©

SECTION A

1. Check that the answer sheet provided is for Chemistry Higher (Section A).

2. Fill in the details required on the answer sheet.

3. **In questions 1 to 40 of this part of the paper, an answer is given by indicating the choice A, B, C or D by a stroke made in INK in the appropriate place in Part 1 of the answer sheet—see the sample question below.**

4. **For each question there is only ONE correct answer.**

5. Rough working, if required, should be done only on this question paper, or on the rough working sheet provided—**not** on the answer sheet.

6. At the end of the examination the answer sheet for Section A **must** be placed **inside** the front cover of this answer book.

This part of the paper is worth 40 marks.

SAMPLE QUESTION

To show that the ink in a ball-pen consists of a mixture of dyes, the method of separation would be

        A   fractional distillation

        B   chromatography

        C   fractional crystallisation

        D   filtration.

The correct answer is B—chromatography. A **heavy** vertical line should be drawn joining the two dots in the appropriate box in the column headed **B** as shown **in the example on the answer sheet**.

If, after you have recorded your answer, you decide that you have made an error and wish to make a change, you should cancel the original answer and put a vertical stroke in the box you now consider to be correct. Thus, if you want to change an answer **D** to an answer **B**, your answer sheet would look like this:

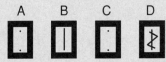

If you want to change back to an answer which has already been scored out, you should **enter a tick (✓)** to the RIGHT of the box of your choice, thus:

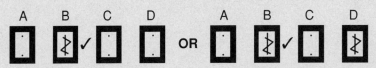

                                                                           Page two

1. Which compound contains **both** a halide ion and a transition metal ion?

   A   Iron oxide

   B   Potassium permanganate

   C   Nickel bromide

   D   Copper iodate

2. A part of the molecular structure for PTFE is shown.

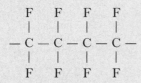

   This is classed as a

   A   synthetic addition polymer

   B   synthetic condensation polymer

   C   natural condensation polymer

   D   natural addition polymer.

3. Four metals **W**, **X**, **Y** and **Z** and their compounds were tested as described.

   (i) Only **X**, **Y** and **Z** reacted with dilute hydrochloric acid.

   (ii) The oxides of **W**, **X** and **Y** were reduced to the metal when heated with carbon powder. The oxide of **Z** did not react.

   (iii) A displacement reaction occurred when **X** was added to an aqueous solution of the nitrate of **Y**.

   The correct order of reactivity of these metals (most reactive first) is

   A   **W, Y, X, Z**

   B   **W, X, Y, Z**

   C   **Z, X, Y, W**

   D   **Z, Y, X, W**.

4. What is the amount of iron(II) ions in $40\,cm^3$ of $0.1\,mol\,l^{-1}$ iron(II) sulphate solution?

   A 0.1 mol

   B 0.01 mol

   C 0.04 mol

   D 0.004 mol

5. Some pieces of equipment are shown below.

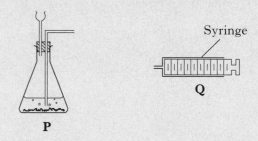

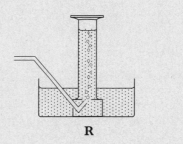

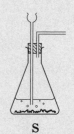

   You are asked to measure accurately the volume of carbon dioxide produced every minute when chalk and acid react together.

   Which of the following combinations of pieces of equipment is the **best** one to use?

   A   **P** and **Q**

   B   **S** and **Q**

   C   **P** and **R**

   D   **S** and **R**

6. The same reaction was carried out at four different temperatures. The table shows the times taken for the reaction to occur.

Temperature/°C	20	30	40	50
Time/s	60	30	14	5

   The results show that

   A   a small rise in temperature results in a large increase in reaction rate

   B   the activation energy increases with increasing temperature

   C   the rate of the reaction is directly proportional to the temperature

   D   the reaction is endothermic.

7. When copper carbonate reacts with excess acid, carbon dioxide is produced. The curves shown were obtained under different conditions.

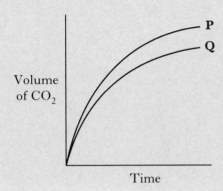

The change from **P** to **Q** could be brought about by

A   increasing the concentration of the acid

B   decreasing the mass of copper carbonate

C   decreasing the particle size of the copper carbonate

D   adding a catalyst.

8. Refer to the potential energy diagram below.

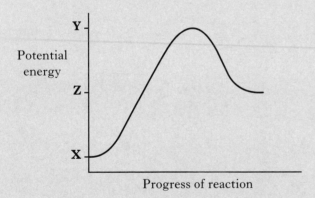

The energy of activation (E_A) for the forward reaction is given by

A   **Y**

B   **Z – X**

C   **Y – X**

D   **Y – Z**.

9. Which equation represents the first ionisation energy of a diatomic element, X_2?

A $\frac{1}{2}X_2(s) \rightarrow X^+(g)$

B $\frac{1}{2}X_2(g) \rightarrow X^-(g)$

C $X(s) \rightarrow X^-(g)$

D $X(g) \rightarrow X^+(g)$

10. The spike graph shows the variation in the first ionisation energy with atomic number for sixteen consecutive elements in the Periodic Table. The element at which the spike graph starts is **not** specified.

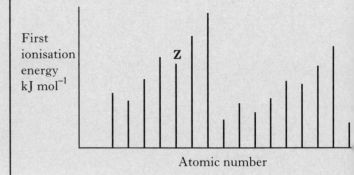

In which group of the Periodic Table is element **Z**?

A   1

B   3

C   5

D   6

11. Which chloride is most likely to be soluble in tetrachloromethane, CCl_4?

A   Barium chloride

B   Caesium chloride

C   Calcium chloride

D   Phosphorus chloride

12. Carbon dioxide is a gas at room temperature while silicon dioxide is a solid because

A   van der Waals' forces are much weaker than covalent bonds

B   carbon dioxide contains double covalent bonds and silicon dioxide contains single covalent bonds

C   carbon-oxygen bonds are less polar than silicon-oxygen bonds

D   the relative formula mass of carbon dioxide is less than that of silicon dioxide.

13. Which oxide would be a solid at room temperature (20 °C) and a gas at 400 °C?

You may wish to use the data booklet.

A   Fluorine oxide

B   Phosphorus oxide

C   Magnesium oxide

D   Boron oxide

14. Which of the following has the same volume as 16 g of sulphur dioxide gas?

(All volumes are measured under the same conditions of temperature and pressure.)

A   1 g of helium gas

B   1 g of hydrogen gas

C   10 g of neon gas

D   16 g of oxygen gas

15. The mass of one mole of sodium is 23 g.

What is the mass of one sodium atom?

A $6{\cdot}02 \times 10^{23}$ g

B $6{\cdot}02 \times 10^{-23}$ g

C $3{\cdot}82 \times 10^{-23}$ g

D $3{\cdot}82 \times 10^{-24}$ g

16. What volume of oxygen, in litres, is required for complete combustion of 1 litre of butane?

A   1

B   4

C   6.5

D   13

17. Avogadro's Constant is the same as the number of

A   electrons in $0{\cdot}5$ mol of hydrogen atoms

B   atoms in $0{\cdot}5$ mol of chlorine gas

C   molecules in $0{\cdot}5$ mol of carbon monoxide

D   ions in $0{\cdot}5$ mol of sodium oxide.

18. Which molecule is **most** likely to be found in petrol?

A CH_4

B C_3H_8

C C_8H_{18}

D $C_{14}H_{30}$

19. Some biological materials, under anaerobic conditions, ferment to produce

A   methane

B   ethene

C   methanol

D   ethanoic acid.

20. Which of the following is an ester?

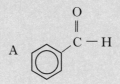

21. Which compound has isomeric forms?

A C_2H_3Cl

B C_2H_5Cl

C C_2HCl_3

D $C_2H_4Cl_2$

22. Which equation represents an addition reaction?

A $CH_3OH + O_2 \rightarrow HCOOH + H_2O$

B $CH_3CH_2OH \rightarrow CH_2CH_2 + H_2O$

C $CH_2CH_2 + H_2O \rightarrow CH_3CH_2OH$

D $CH_3CH_3 \rightarrow CH_2CH_2 + H_2$

23. Which structural formula represents a tertiary alcohol?

A $CH_3-CH_2-CH_2-\underset{\underset{OH}{|}}{\overset{\overset{H}{|}}{C}}-CH_3$

B $CH_3-CH_2-\underset{\underset{OH}{|}}{\overset{\overset{H}{|}}{C}}-CH_2-CH_3$

C $CH_3-\underset{\underset{OH}{|}}{\overset{\overset{CH_3}{|}}{C}}-CH_2-CH_3$

D $CH_3-\underset{\underset{CH_3}{|}}{\overset{\overset{CH_3}{|}}{C}}-CH_2-OH$

24. In the atmosphere, ozone forms a protective layer that absorbs ultraviolet radiation from the sun.

Which statement about ozone is true?

A Ozone is an element.

B Ozone is made up of diatomic molecules.

C Ozone is made by the reaction of nitrogen with oxygen.

D Ozone is mainly produced by the burning of fossil fuels.

25. Part of a polymer is shown.

$-\underset{\underset{H}{|}}{\overset{\overset{H}{|}}{C}}-\underset{\underset{H}{|}}{\overset{\overset{C_2H_5}{|}}{C}}-\underset{\underset{H}{|}}{\overset{\overset{H}{|}}{C}}-\underset{\underset{H}{|}}{\overset{\overset{H}{|}}{C}}-\underset{\underset{H}{|}}{\overset{\overset{H}{|}}{C}}-\underset{\underset{H}{|}}{\overset{\overset{C_2H_5}{|}}{C}}-\underset{\underset{H}{|}}{\overset{\overset{H}{|}}{C}}-\underset{\underset{H}{|}}{\overset{\overset{H}{|}}{C}}-$

Which pair of alkenes was used as monomers?

A Ethene and propene

B Ethene and but-1-ene

C Propene and but-1-ene

D Ethene and but-2-ene

26. Synthesis gas is a mixture of carbon monoxide and hydrogen.

It can be made by

A fractional distillation of liquid air

B burning coal in excess air

C burning natural gas in excess air

D reacting natural gas with steam.

27. The uses of polymers are related to their properties.

Which polymer is used to make ropes due to its strength?

A Poly(ethenol)

B Poly(ethyne)

C Kevlar

D Biopol

28. Fats and oils can be classified as

A soaps

B fatty acids

C esters

D polyesters.

29. The structural formula for glycerol is

A $\underset{CH_2OH}{\overset{CH_2OH}{\underset{|}{\overset{|}{CHOH}}}}$

B $\underset{CH_2OH}{\overset{CH_2OH}{\underset{|}{\overset{|}{CH_2}}}}$

C $\overset{CH_2OH}{\underset{CH_2OH}{|}}$

D $\underset{CH_2COOH}{\overset{CH_2OH}{\underset{|}{\overset{|}{CHOH}}}}$

30. The conversion of linoleic acid, $C_{18}H_{32}O_2$, into stearic acid, $C_{18}H_{36}O_2$, is likely to be achieved by

A hydrogenation

B hydrolysis

C hydration

D dehydrogenation.

31. Which element is **not** a raw material in the chemical industry?

A Nitrogen

B Oxygen

C Sodium

D Sulphur

32. Consider the reaction pathway shown below.

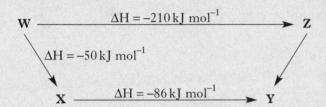

According to Hess's Law, the ΔH value, in $kJ\,mol^{-1}$, for reaction **Z** to **Y** is

A +74

B −74

C +346

D −346.

33. Given that the enthalpies of combustion of carbon, hydrogen and ethane are **X**, **Y** and **Z** respectively, the enthalpy change for the reaction

$$2C(s) \quad + \quad 3H_2(g) \quad \rightarrow \quad C_2H_6(g)$$

will be

A $(2\mathbf{X} + 3\mathbf{Y} - \mathbf{Z})$

B $(2\mathbf{X} + 3\mathbf{Y} + \mathbf{Z})$

C $(\mathbf{X} + \mathbf{Y} - \mathbf{Z})$

D $(-2\mathbf{X} - 3\mathbf{Y} + \mathbf{Z})$.

34. Which entry in the table shows the effect of a catalyst on the reaction rates and position of equilibrium in a reversible reaction?

	Rate of forward reaction	Rate of reverse reaction	Position of equilibrium
A	increased	unchanged	moves right
B	increased	increased	unchanged
C	increased	decreased	moves right
D	unchanged	unchanged	unchanged

35. $2NO(g) + O_2(g) \rightleftharpoons 2NO_2(g)$
$$\Delta H = -560\,kJ\,mol^{-1}$$

Which two conditions favour the formation of NO_2?

A High temperature, high pressure

B High temperature, low pressure

C Low temperature, high pressure

D Low temperature, low pressure

36. Lowering the pH of a solution from 13 to 10 causes the concentration of the $OH^-(aq)$ ions to

A increase by a factor of 3

B increase by a factor of 1000

C decrease by a factor of 3

D decrease by a factor of 1000.

37. Which of the following is the best description of a $0 \cdot 1\,mol\,l^{-1}$ solution of ethanoic acid?

A Dilute solution of a weak acid

B Dilute solution of a strong acid

C Concentrated solution of a weak acid

D Concentrated solution of a strong acid

38. Which solution has a pH lower than 7?

A Sodium chloride

B Lithium chloride

C Potassium chloride

D Ammonium chloride

39. $^2_1H + ^3_1H \rightarrow ^4_2He + ^1_0n$

The above process represents

A   nuclear fission

B   nuclear fusion

C   proton capture

D   beta emission.

40. Which particle will be formed when an atom of $^{211}_{83}Bi$ loses an alpha particle and the decay product then loses a beta particle?

A $^{210}_{79}Au$

B $^{209}_{80}Hg$

C $^{209}_{81}Tl$

D $^{207}_{82}Pb$

Candidates are reminded that the answer sheet MUST be returned INSIDE the front cover of this answer book.

Marks

SECTION B

1. Hydrocarbons which are suitable for unleaded petrol are produced in oil refineries. An example of one of the reactions which takes place is shown.

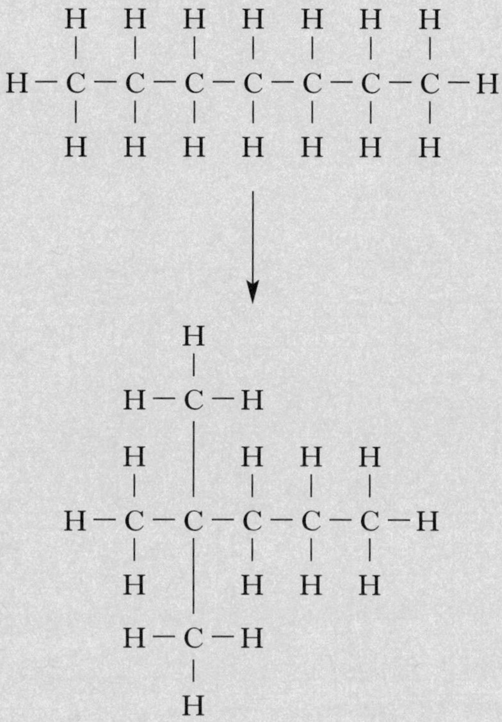

(a) What name is given to the industrial process in which reactions like the above occur?

1

(b) State the systematic name for the product of the reaction shown.

1

(c) What structural feature of the product makes it suitable for use in unleaded petrol?

1

(3)

Marks

2. The radioisotope, sodium-24, can be made in a nuclear reactor by bombarding element **X** with neutrons.

$$^a_b\text{X} \quad + \quad ^1_0\text{n} \quad \rightarrow \quad ^{24}_{11}\text{Na}$$

(a) Identify element **X** and write values for **a** and **b**.

1

(b) The graph shows how the mass of a sample of sodium-24 varies with time.

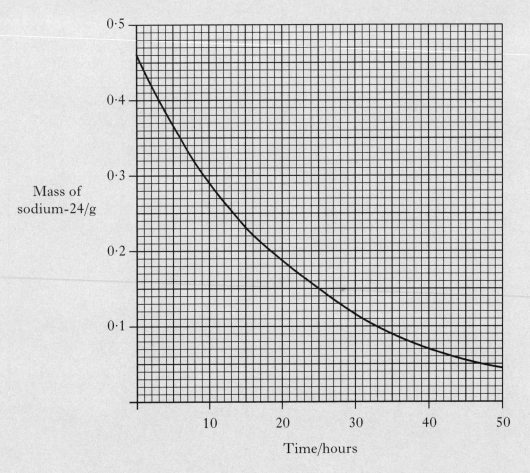

(i) What is the half-life of sodium-24?

1

Marks

2. **(b) (continued)**

    (ii) Calculate the average rate of decay of sodium-24 over the first ten hours.

    Show your working clearly.

1

(c) Two samples of ^{24}Na and $^{24}NaCl$ have the same mass.
    Why are their intensities of radiation different?

1
(4)

Marks

3. Butan-1-ol reacts in different ways.

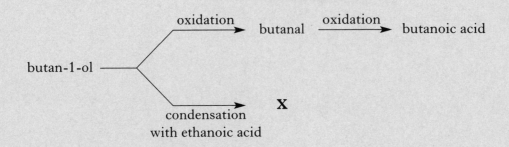

(*a*) Name a reagent that could be used to oxidise butan-1-ol to butanal.

1

(*b*) Name an isomer of butanal that **cannot** be oxidised to butanoic acid.

1

(*c*) Draw a structural formula for ester **X** produced by the condensation of butan-1-ol with ethanoic acid.

1

(3)

Marks

4. Sulphur dioxide dissolves in water to form a weak acid.

$$SO_2(aq) \quad + \quad H_2O(\ell) \quad \rightleftharpoons \quad 2H^+(aq) \quad + \quad SO_3^{2-}(aq)$$

The concentration of added sulphur dioxide can be determined using the following apparatus.

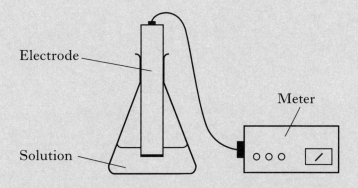

(*a*) What is meant by a weak acid?

1

(*b*) Why is sulphuric acid added to the solution **before** determining the concentration of added sulphur dioxide?

1

(*c*) A solution of sulphur dioxide has a hydrogen ion concentration of 1×10^{-5} mol l^{-1}.

What is the pH of the solution?

1

(3)

Marks

5. (*a*) Ethane-1,2-diol can be polymerised with terephthalic acid to form a synthetic polymer.

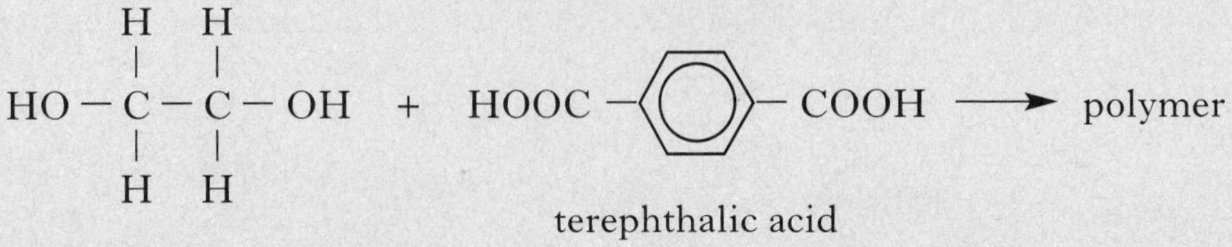

$$HO-\underset{\underset{H}{|}}{\overset{\overset{H}{|}}{C}}-\underset{\underset{H}{|}}{\overset{\overset{H}{|}}{C}}-OH \quad + \quad HOOC-\langle \bigcirc \rangle-COOH \quad \longrightarrow \quad \text{polymer}$$

terephthalic acid

(i) Write the molecular formula for terephthalic acid.

1

(ii) Draw a section of polymer showing **one** molecule of each monomer joined together.

1

(iii) Why would this polymer be formed as a fibre and **not** a resin?

1

DO NOT WRITE IN THIS MARGIN

Marks

5. (continued)

(*b*) Amino acids polymerise to form natural polymers.

(i) Give the name for polymers made up of many amino acids linked together. **1**

(ii) Name the type of polymerisation which takes place. **1**

(5)

Marks

6. The American scientist Linus Pauling devised the electronegativity scale.

    (*a*) Explain the trend in the electronegativity values of the Group 7 elements.

    2

    (*b*) Use the electronegativity values to explain why carbon disulphide contains pure covalent bonds.

    1

    (3)

Marks

7. Hydrogen peroxide solution decomposes to produce oxygen gas.

$$2H_2O_2(aq) \longrightarrow 2H_2O(\ell) + O_2(g)$$

This reaction can be used to study the effect of varying pH on the activity of catalase, an enzyme found in potatoes.

(*a*) Draw a diagram of the apparatus that could be used for this study.

Clearly label the diagram.

1

(*b*) Calculate the volume of oxygen, in litres, produced by the complete decomposition of a solution containing $3\cdot4$ g of hydrogen peroxide.

(Take the molar volume of oxygen as $24\cdot0$ litres.)

Show your working clearly.

2

(3)

Marks

8. The following results are taken from the notebook of a student who was trying to confirm Hess's Law.

Experiment 1– Addition of 1·6g of sodium hydroxide solid to 50cm^3 of 1 mol ℓ^{-1} hydrochloric acid

$$NaOH(s) + HC\ell(aq) \rightarrow NaC\ell(aq) + H_2O(\ell)$$

Mass = 50g

Initial temperature of $HC\ell(aq)$ = 21·7°C

Highest temperature during experiment = 29·9°C

ΔT = $\underline{8·2C°}$

Experiment 2– Addition of 25cm^3 of 2 mol ℓ^{-1} sodium hydroxide solution to 25cm^3 of 2 mol ℓ^{-1} hydrochloric acid

$$NaOH(aq) + HC\ell(aq) \rightarrow NaC\ell(aq) + H_2O(\ell)$$

Mass = 50g

Initial temperature of $HC\ell(aq)$ - T_1 = 21·7°C

Initial temperature of $NaOH(aq)$ - T_2 = 22·1°C

Highest temperature during experiment = 28·6°C

ΔT =

(*a*) (i) In **experiment 1**, find by calculation which reactant is in excess.
Show your working clearly.

2

DO NOT
WRITE IN
THIS
MARGIN

Marks

8. (*a*) (continued)

(ii) In **experiment 1**, calculate the energy released during the reaction.

1

(*b*) Calculate ΔT for **experiment 2**.

1

(*c*) Outline a third experiment which would have to be carried out in order to confirm Hess's Law.

1
(5)

Marks

9. A student studied the effect of varying the temperature on the rate of reaction between oxalic acid and an acidified solution of potassium permanganate.

$$5(COOH)_2(aq) + 6H^+(aq) + 2MnO_4^-(aq) \longrightarrow 2Mn^{2+}(aq) + 10CO_2(g) + 8H_2O(\ell)$$

(a) What colour change can be used to follow the course of the reaction?

1

(b) With the help of a labelled energy distribution diagram, explain why the rate of a reaction increases with increasing temperature.

2

(3)

Marks

10. The reaction of solid calcium hydride with water, to form calcium hydroxide and hydrogen, is often used to supply the gas in weather balloons.

(*a*) Balance the equation for the reaction of calcium hydride with water.

$$CaH_2 \quad + \quad H_2O \quad \longrightarrow \quad Ca(OH)_2 \quad + \quad H_2$$

1

(*b*) Draw a diagram of the apparatus that could be used to show that the hydride ion in calcium hydride has a negative charge.

Clearly label the diagram.

2

(3)

DO NO
WRITE
THIS
MARGI

Marks

11. Titanium is a very useful metal. It has many uses, from components of spacecraft to spectacle frames.

The diagram shows steps in the manufacture of titanium.

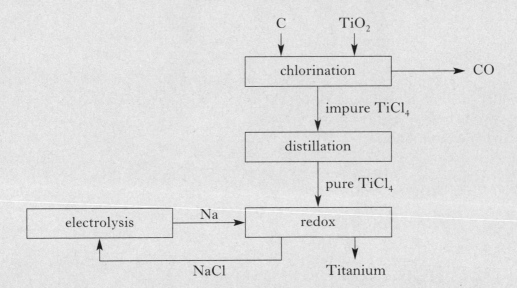

(a) In this diagram, sodium is recycled.

Add a labelled arrow to the diagram to show how the process could be made even more economical.

1

(b) $TiCl_4$ can be separated from impurities by fractional distillation because it is volatile.

What does this suggest about the type of bonding in $TiCl_4$?

1

(c) Give another name for the redox reaction to produce titanium.

1

(3)

Marks

12. Maleic acid and fumaric acid have the same molecular formula. Their structures are different because rotation is not possible about the carbon-carbon double bond.

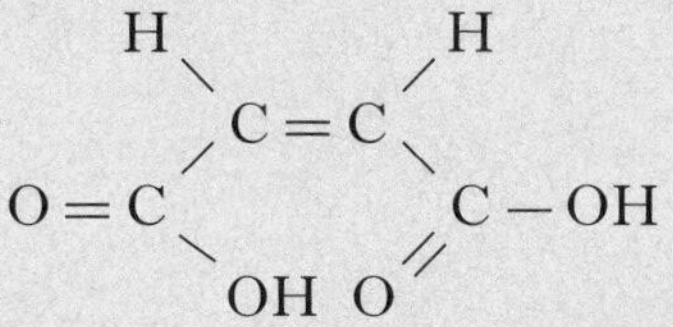

maleic acid
mp 157 °C

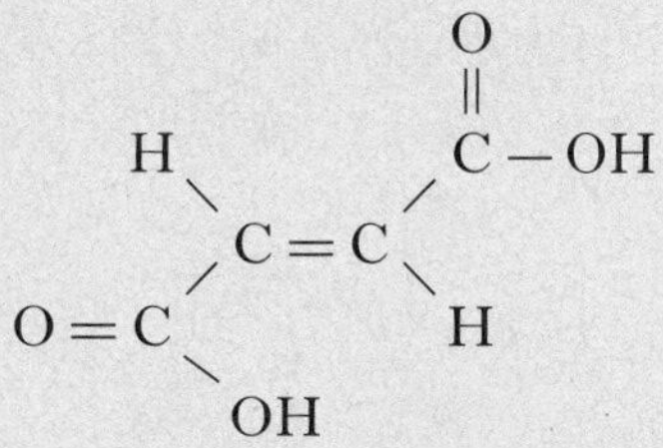

fumaric acid
mp 287 °C

(a) Melting points can be used to compare the strength of intermolecular forces in covalent compounds.

   (i) Why is the melting point of fumaric acid higher than that of maleic acid?

1

   (ii) Name the alkane that should be used to compare the strength of the intermolecular forces in alkanes with maleic and fumaric acids.

1

(b) On heating to 167 °C, maleic acid can change shape and undergo the following reaction.

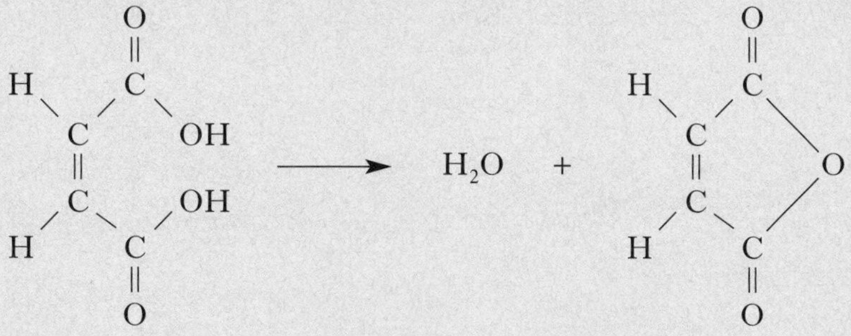

H_2O +

Name the type of reaction taking place.

1

(3)

    Page twenty-three

Marks

13. The first step in the industrial extraction of aluminium is to obtain aluminium oxide from the ore called bauxite.

The ore is crushed. It is then digested, under pressure, with sodium hydroxide solution. The resulting mixture is filtered and the residue (containing large amounts of iron(III) oxide) is removed.

The filtrate is seeded with a little aluminium hydroxide in order to produce **large** amounts of aluminium hydroxide. Sodium hydroxide solution is also formed.

The aluminium hydroxide passes to a rotary kiln where it is roasted to form pure aluminium oxide.

(*a*) Complete the following flow chart, in order to summarise the production of aluminium oxide.

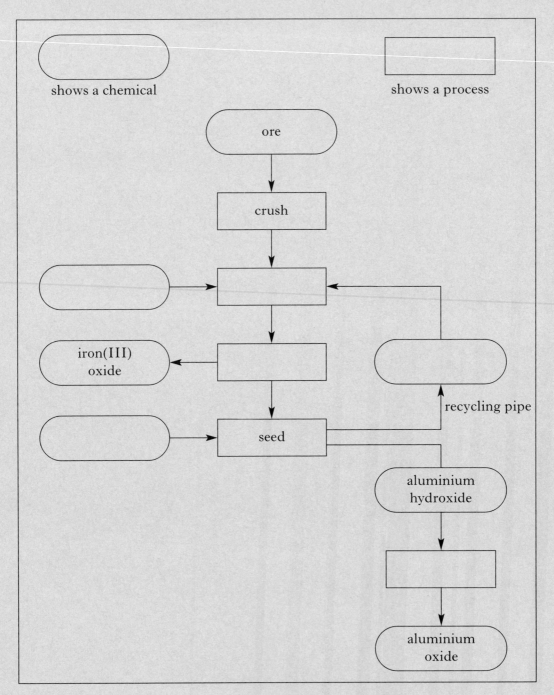

2

Marks

13. **(continued)**

(*b*) Electrolysis of the molten aluminium oxide produces aluminium at the negative electrode.

Calculate the approximate time required to produce 100 kg of aluminium using a steady current of 40 000 A.

Show your working clearly.

3

(5)

DO NOT
WRITE
THIS
MARGIN

Marks

14. In a mass spectrometer, the energy of an electron beam can break bonds in molecules to form fragments containing groups of atoms. The positions of the peaks (or lines) in a mass spectrum correspond to the masses of the fragments which are formed.

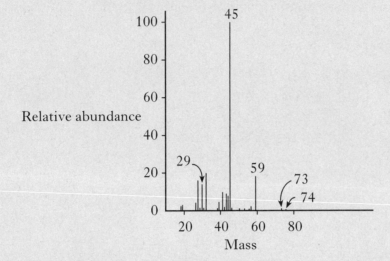

In the mass spectrum shown, the peaks at masses 29, 45 and 59 are formed by the breaking of carbon to carbon bonds in:

```
        H   H   H   H
        |   |   |   |
  H  —  C — C — C — C — H
        |   |   |   |
        H   H   OH  H
```

(a) Name the above compound.

1

(b) Complete the table below.

Relative mass	Formula of fragment
29	C_2H_5
45	C_2H_4OH
59	

1

(c) What causes the peaks at masses just below the main peak at 45, eg at 44, 43, 42, 41?

1

Marks

15. Prefixes can be used to indicate the number of atoms in a molecule.

Term	Number of atoms in the molecule	Example
diatomic	2	hydrogen chloride
triatomic	3	carbon dioxide
tetra-atomic	4	sulphur trioxide
penta-atomic	5	tetrachloromethane
hexa-atomic	6	phosphorus pentachloride

(*a*) What term is used to describe the following molecule?

1

(*b*) Name a hexa-atomic molecule, containing carbon, which will decolourise bromine water rapidly.

1

(*c*) Write the formula for a carbon compound consisting of penta-atomic molecules with a molecular mass of 85.

1

(3)

Marks

16. The purity of iron(II) salts can be found by titration with acidified potassium permanganate solution.

Equations:

$$Fe^{2+}(aq) \longrightarrow Fe^{3+}(aq) + e^-$$

$$MnO_4^-(aq) + 8H^+(aq) + 5e^- \longrightarrow Mn^{2+}(aq) + 4H_2O(\ell)$$

(a) The picture shows a trainee technician taking a burette reading while carrying out a permanganate titration.

Identify **four** points of bad practice in his technique.

2

DO NOT WRITE IN THIS MARGIN

Marks

16. (continued)

(*b*) A pupil was given a sample of impure iron(II) sulphate, $FeSO_4.7H_2O$, and used this to prepare $250\,cm^3$ of solution for the titration.

It was found that $9{\cdot}5\,cm^3$ of $0{\cdot}01\ mol\,l^{-1}$ acidified potassium permanganate solution was required to oxidise $25\,cm^3$ of the iron(II) sulphate solution.

Calculate the mass of iron(II) sulphate in the sample.

Show your working clearly. **3**

(5)

Marks

17. (*a*) The idea of **oxidation number** leads to a systematic method of naming inorganic compounds.

The systematic name of $KClO_3$ is potassium chlorate(V) where the Roman numeral in brackets represents the oxidition number of the chlorine atom.

Simplified rules for working out oxidation numbers are:

all Group 1 metals have an oxidation number of +1;

oxygen has an oxidation number of –2;

the sum of the oxidation numbers of all atoms in the formula of a compound is zero.

Complete the table below.

Formula	Oxidation number of non-oxygen atom in the negative ion	Systematic name	Charge on the negative ion
$KClO_3$	+5	potassium chlorate(V)	–1
Na_2SO_4	+6		–2
	+7	potassium iodate(VII)	–1
Na_3PO_4			

2

(*b*) In acid solution, potassium chlorate(V), $KClO_3(aq)$, oxidises sodium iodide.

Write an ion-electron equation for the oxidation reaction.

1

(3)

[END OF QUESTION PAPER]

2000 HIGHER

FOR OFFICIAL USE

Total
Section B

X012/301

NATIONAL
QUALIFICATIONS
2000

WEDNESDAY, 7 JUNE
9.00 AM – 11.30 AM

CHEMISTRY
HIGHER

Fill in these boxes and read what is printed below.

Full name of centre

Town

Forename(s)

Surname

Date of birth
Day Month Year   Scottish candidate number   Number of seat

Reference may be made to the Chemistry Higher and Advanced Higher Data Booklet (1999 edition).

SECTION A—Part 1 Questions 1–30 and Part 2 Questions 31–34

Instructions for completion of **Part 1** and **Part 2** are given on pages two and eight respectively.

SECTION B

1 All questions should be attempted.

2 The questions may be answered in any order but all answers are to be written in the spaces provided in this answer book, and must be written clearly and legibly in ink.

3 Rough work, if any should be necessary, should be written in this book and then scored through when the fair copy has been written.

4 Additional space for answers and rough work will be found at the end of the book. If further space is required, supplementary sheets may be obtained from the invigilator and should be inserted inside the **front** cover of this book.

5 The size of the space provided for an answer should not be taken as an indication of how much to write. It is not necessary to use all the space.

6 Before leaving the examination room you must give this book to the invigilator. If you do not, you may lose all the marks for this paper.

SCOTTISH
QUALIFICATIONS
AUTHORITY

SECTION A

PART 1

Check that the answer sheet provided is for Chemistry Higher (Section A).

Fill in the details required on the answer sheet.

In questions 1 to 30 of this part of the paper, an answer is given by indicating the choice A, B, C or D by a stroke made in INK in the appropriate place in Part 1 of the answer sheet—see the sample question below.

For each question there is only ONE correct answer.

Rough working, if required, should be done only on this question paper, or on the rough working sheet provided—**not** on the answer sheet.

At the end of the examination the answer sheet for Section A **must** be placed **inside** this answer book.

This part of the paper is worth 30 marks.

SAMPLE QUESTION

To show that the ink in a ball-pen consists of a mixture of dyes, the method of separation would be

        A   fractional distillation

        B   chromatography

        C   fractional crystallisation

        D   filtration.

The correct answer is B—chromatography. A **heavy** vertical line should be drawn joining the two dots in the appropriate box in the column headed **B** as shown **in the example on the answer sheet**.

If, after you have recorded your answer, you decide that you have made an error and wish to make a change, you should cancel the original answer and put a vertical stroke in the box you now consider to be correct. Thus, if you want to change an answer **D** to an answer **B**, your answer sheet would look like this:

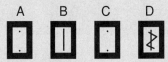

If you want to change back to an answer which has already been scored out, you should **enter a tick (✓)** to the RIGHT of the box of your choice, thus:

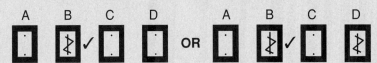

1. Which chloride conducts electricity when molten?

   A   Calcium chloride

   B   Nitrogen chloride

   C   Phosphorus chloride

   D   Silicon chloride

2. Which pair of solutions is most likely to produce a precipitate when mixed?

   A   Magnesium nitrate + sodium chloride

   B   Magnesium nitrate + sodium sulphate

   C   Silver nitrate + sodium chloride

   D   Silver nitrate + sodium sulphate

3. What volume of $0.4 \, mol \, l^{-1}$ sodium hydroxide solution is needed to neutralise $50 \, cm^3$ of $0.1 \, mol \, l^{-1}$ sulphuric acid?

   A $25 \, cm^3$

   B $50 \, cm^3$

   C $100 \, cm^3$

   D $200 \, cm^3$

4. Particles with the same electron arrangement are said to be isoelectronic.

   Which compound contains ions which are isoelectronic?

   A Na_2O

   B   LiF

   C   CaO

   D $CaBr_2$

5. The graph shows the variation of concentration of a reactant with time as a reaction proceeds.

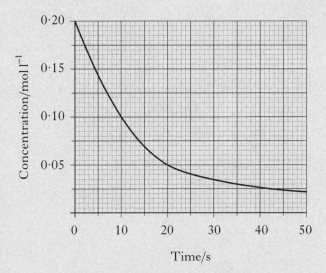

   What is the average reaction rate during the first 20 s?

   A $0.0025 \, mol \, l^{-1} s^{-1}$

   B $0.0050 \, mol \, l^{-1} s^{-1}$

   C $0.0075 \, mol \, l^{-1} s^{-1}$

   D $0.0150 \, mol \, l^{-1} s^{-1}$

6. Excess zinc was added to $100 \, cm^3$ of hydrochloric acid, concentration $1 \, mol \, l^{-1}$.

   Graph I refers to this reaction.

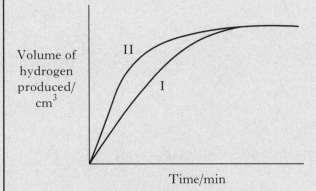

   Graph II could be for

   A   excess zinc reacting with $100 \, cm^3$ of hydrochloric acid, concentration $2 \, mol \, l^{-1}$

   B   excess zinc reacting with $100 \, cm^3$ of sulphuric acid, concentration $1 \, mol \, l^{-1}$

   C   excess zinc reacting with $100 \, cm^3$ of ethanoic acid, concentration $1 \, mol \, l^{-1}$

   D   excess magnesium reacting with $100 \, cm^3$ of hydrochloric acid, concentration $1 \, mol \, l^{-1}$.

7.

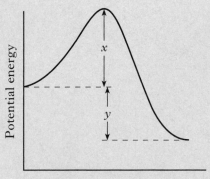

Reaction pathway

The enthalpy change for the forward reaction can be represented by

A x

B y

C $x + y$

D $x - y$.

8. The difference between the atomic size of sodium and chlorine is mainly due to the difference in the

A   number of electrons

B   number of protons

C   number of neutrons

D   mass of each atom.

9. In which molecule will the chlorine atom carry a partial positive charge ($\delta +$)?

A   Cl – Br

B   Cl – Cl

C   Cl – F

D   Cl – I

10. Which statement may be correctly applied to silicon dioxide?

A   It consists of discrete molecules.

B   It has a covalent network structure.

C   It is similar in structure to carbon dioxide.

D   Van der Waals' attractions are important to its structure.

11. Which of the following contains one mole of neutrons?

A   1g of $^{1}_{1}$H

B   1g of $^{12}_{6}$C

C   2g of $^{24}_{12}$Mg

D   2g of $^{22}_{10}$Ne

12. Which ester is an isomer of butanoic acid?

A   Ethyl ethanoate

B   Ethyl methanoate

C   Ethyl propanoate

D   Propyl ethanoate

13. What product(s) would be expected upon dehydration of the following alcohol?

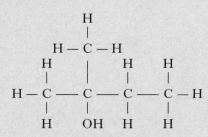

A   2-methylbut-2-ene only

B   2-methylbut-2-ene and
    2-methylbut-1-ene

C   2-methylbut-1-ene only

D   3-methylbut-1-ene and
    2-methylbut-1-ene

14. Which consumer product is least likely to contain esters?

A   Flavourings

B   Perfumes

C   Solvents

D   Toothpastes

15. Part of a polymer chain is shown below.

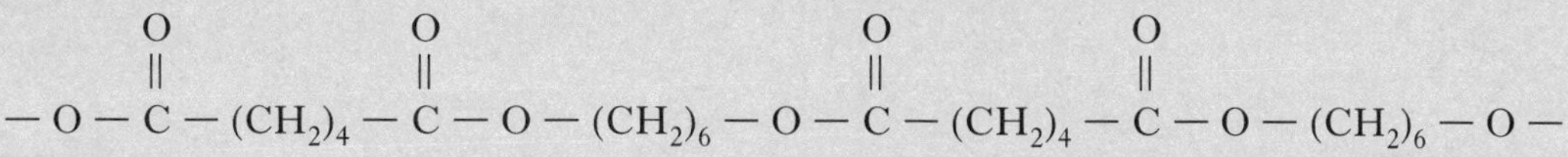

$$-O-\overset{\overset{O}{\|}}{C}-(CH_2)_4-\overset{\overset{O}{\|}}{C}-O-(CH_2)_6-O-\overset{\overset{O}{\|}}{C}-(CH_2)_4-\overset{\overset{O}{\|}}{C}-O-(CH_2)_6-O-$$

Which compound, when added to the reactants during polymerisation, would stop the polymer chain from getting too long?

A
$$HO-\overset{\overset{O}{\|}}{C}-(CH_2)_4-\overset{\overset{O}{\|}}{C}-OH$$

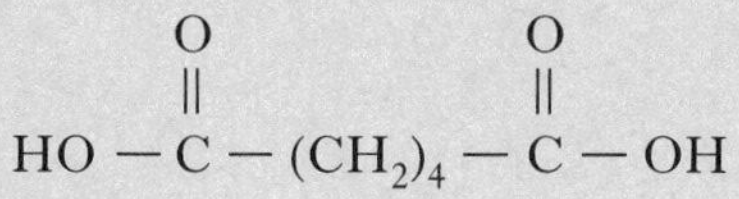

B $HO-(CH_2)_6-OH$

C
$$HO-(CH_2)_5-\overset{\overset{O}{\|}}{C}-OH$$

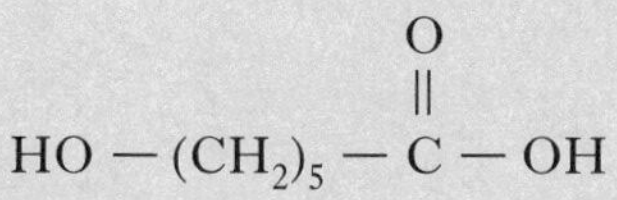

D CH_3-OH

---

16. Ethene is used in the manufacture of addition polymers.

What type of reaction is used to produce ethene from ethane?

A Addition

B Cracking

C Hydrogenation

D Oxidation

17. Which polymer can dissolve in water?

A Poly(ethenol)

B Poly(ethyne)

C Biopol

D Kevlar

18. Amino acids are converted into proteins by

A hydration

B hydrolysis

C hydrogenation

D condensation.

19. Fats have higher melting points than oils because comparing fats and oils

A fats have more hydrogen bonds

B fats have more cross-links between molecules

C fat molecules are more loosely packed

D fat molecules are more saturated.

20. The costs involved in the industrial production of a chemical are made up of fixed costs and variable costs.

Which of the following is most likely to be classified as a variable cost?

A The cost of land rental

B The cost of plant construction

C The cost of labour

D The cost of raw materials

[Turn over

21. $N_2(g) + 2O_2(g) \rightarrow 2NO_2(g)$ $\Delta H = +88kJ$
    $N_2(g) + 2O_2(g) \rightarrow N_2O_4(g)$ $\Delta H = +10kJ$

    The enthalpy change for the reaction

    $2NO_2(g) \rightarrow N_2O_4(g)$ will be

    A +98 kJ

    B +78 kJ

    C −78 kJ

    D −98 kJ.

22. Chemical reactions are in a state of dynamic equilibrium only when

    A the rate of the forward reaction equals that of the backward reaction

    B the concentrations of reactants and products are equal

    C the activation energies of the forward and backward reactions are equal

    D the reaction involves zero enthalpy change.

23. Under the conditions used industrially, ethene and steam react as follows.

    $$C_2H_4(g) + H_2O(g) \rightleftharpoons C_2H_5OH(g)$$
    $$\Delta H = \pm 46 kJ mol^{\pm 1}$$

    Which set of conditions would give the best yield of ethanol at equilibrium?

    A High temperature, low pressure

    B High temperature, high pressure

    C Low temperature, high pressure

    D Low temperature, low pressure

24. Which of the following is the best description of a 0.1 mol l^{-1} solution of hydrochloric acid?

    A Dilute solution of a weak acid

    B Dilute solution of a strong acid

    C Concentrated solution of a weak acid

    D Concentrated solution of a strong acid

25. A trout fishery owner added limestone to his loch to combat the effects of acid rain. He managed to raise the pH of the water from 4 to 6.

    The concentration of the $H^+(aq)$

    A increased by a factor of 2

    B increased by a factor of 100

    C decreased by a factor of 2

    D decreased by a factor of 100.

26. Which of the following is the same for equal volumes of 0.1 mol l^{-1} solutions of sodium hydroxide and ammonia?

    A pH of solution

    B Mass of solute present

    C Conductivity of solution

    D The number of moles of hydrochloric acid needed for neutralisation

27. During a redox process in acid solution, iodate ions, $IO_3^-(aq)$, are converted into iodine, $I_2(aq)$.

    $$IO_3^-(aq) \rightarrow I_2(aq)$$

    The numbers of $H^+(aq)$ and $H_2O\ (\ell)$ required to balance the ion-electron equation for the formation of 1 mol of $I_2(aq)$ are, respectively

    A 6 and 3

    B 3 and 6

    C 12 and 6

    D 6 and 12.

28. The reduction of copper ions during electroplating can be represented as:

    $$Cu^{2+}(aq) + 2e^{\pm} \rightarrow Cu(s)$$

    What is the quantity of electricity needed to produce 0.25 mol of copper?

    A 24 125 C

    B 48 250 C

    C 96 500 C

    D 193 000 C

29. A radioactive atom of a Group 4 element emits one β-particle.

   The decay product will be an atom of an element in

   A Group 3

   B Group 4

   C Group 5

   D Group 6.

30. The half-life of the isotope ^{210}Pb is 21 years.

   What fraction of the original ^{210}Pb atoms will be present after 63 years?

   A 0·5

   B 0·25

   C 0·125

   D 0·0625

[Turn over

SECTION A

PART 2

In questions 31 to 34 of this part of the paper, an answer is given by circling the appropriate letter (or letters) in the answer grids provided on Part 2 of the answer sheet.

In some questions, two letters are required for full marks.

If more than the correct number of answers is given, marks may be deducted.

In some cases the number of correct responses is NOT identified in the question.

This part of the paper is worth 10 marks.

SAMPLE QUESTION

A CH$_4$	B H$_2$	C CO$_2$
D CO	E C$_2$H$_6$	F N$_2$

(a)   Identify the diatomic **compound(s)**.

A	B	C
(D)	E	F

The one correct answer to part (a) is D. This should be circled.

(b)   Identify the **two** substances which burn to produce **both** carbon dioxide **and** water.

(A)	B	C
D	(E)	F

As indicated in this question, there are **two** correct answers to part (b). These are A and E.

Both answers are circled.

(c)   Identify the substance(s) which can **not** be used as a fuel.

A	B	(C)
D	E	(F)

There are **two** correct answers to part (c). These are C and F.

Both answers are circled.

If, after you have recorded your answer, you decide that you have made an error and wish to make a change, you should cancel the original answer and circle the answer you now consider to be correct. Thus, in part (a), if you want to change an answer **D** to an answer **A**, your answer sheet would look like this:

(A)	B	C
~~D~~	E	F

If you want to change back to an answer which has already been scored out, you should enter a tick (✓) in the box of the answer of your choice, thus:

~~A~~	B	C
✓ ~~D~~	E	F

31. The grid shows the concentration of solutions, in $mol\,l^{-1}$.

A		B		C	
	2×10^{-1}		1×10^{-1}		1×10^{-2}

D		E		F	
	1×10^{-3}		2×10^{-12}		1×10^{-12}

(a) Identify the concentration of hydrogen ions in a solution which has a pH of 2.

(b) A solution is made by pipetting $10 \cdot 0\,cm^3$ of $0 \cdot 10\,mol\,l^{-1}$ sodium hydroxide solution into a $100\,cm^3$ standard flask and making up to the mark with distilled water.

Identify the concentration of hydrogen ions in the solution.

32. The grid shows quantities of five different gases.

A		B		C		D		E	
	$7\,g$ CO		$32\,g$ CH_4		$4\,g$ H_2		$32\,g$ SO_2		$17\,g$ NH_3

(a) Identify the **two** gases which occupy the same volume.

(Assume all measurements are made under the same conditions of temperature and pressure.)

(b) Identify the **two** gases which contain the same number of atoms.

[Turn over

33. Many factors influence the rates of reactions.

A		B		C	
particle size of reactants		temperature		surface area available for reaction	
D		E		F	
activation energy		concentration		average kinetic energy of reactant molecules	

(a) Identify the factor which, if increased, causes an increase in the factor shown in box **F**.

(b) Identify the factor(s) which, if increased, would make a reaction slower.

34.

$$\begin{array}{l} CH_2OOCC_{17}H_{35} \\ | \\ CHOOCC_{17}H_{31} \\ | \\ CH_2OOCC_{15}H_{29} \end{array} \xrightarrow{\textbf{X}} \begin{array}{l} CH_2OOCC_{17}H_{35} \\ | \\ CHOOCC_{17}H_{33} \\ | \\ CH_2OOCC_{15}H_{31} \end{array} \xrightarrow{\textbf{Y}} \begin{array}{l} CH_2OH \\ | \\ CHOH \\ | \\ CH_2OH \end{array} + \begin{array}{l} C_{17}H_{35}COOH \\ C_{17}H_{33}COOH \\ C_{15}H_{31}COOH \end{array}$$

A		B		C	
Hydration		Addition		Hydrolysis	
D		E		F	
Oxidation		Hydrogenation		Condensation	

(a) Identify the name which could be applied to reaction **Y**.

(b) Identify the name(s) which could be applied to reaction **X**.

Candidates are reminded that the answer sheet MUST be returned INSIDE this answer book.

[Turn over for Section B]

Marks

SECTION B

1. Petrol is produced by the reforming of a fraction obtained from crude oil.

    One such reforming reaction is:

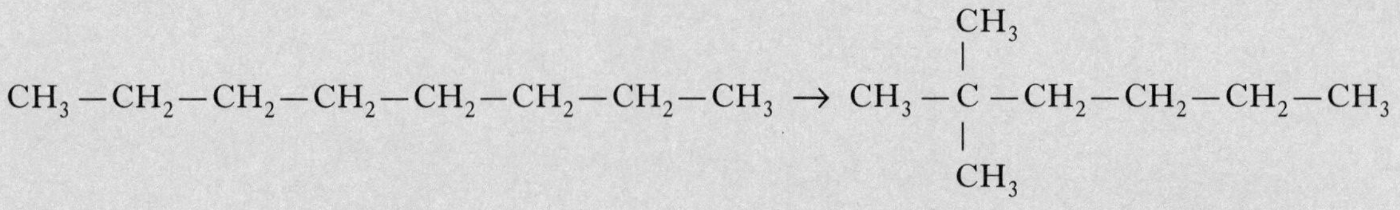

$$CH_3-CH_2-CH_2-CH_2-CH_2-CH_2-CH_2-CH_3 \rightarrow CH_3-\overset{\displaystyle CH_3}{\underset{\displaystyle CH_3}{\overset{|}{\underset{|}{C}}}}-CH_2-CH_2-CH_2-CH_3$$

octane   compound **A**

(a) Which crude oil fraction is reformed to make petrol?

1

(b) Give the systematic name for compound **A**.

1

(c) If the petrol burned in a car engine contains straight-chain alkanes, like octane, a process called "knocking" takes place.

Why does the presence of straight-chain alkanes result in "knocking"?

1

(3)

DO NOT WRITE IN THIS MARGIN

Marks

2. Calcite is a very pure form of calcium carbonate which reacts with nitric acid as follows.

$$CaCO_3(s) \quad + \quad 2HNO_3(aq) \quad \rightarrow \quad Ca(NO_3)_2(aq) \quad + \quad H_2O\,(\ell) \quad + \quad CO_2(g)$$

A 2·14 g piece of calcite was added to 50·0 cm^3 of 0·200 mol l^{-1} nitric acid in a beaker.

(*a*) Calculate the mass of calcite, in grams, left unreacted.

(Show your working clearly.) **2**

(*b*) Describe what could be done to check the result obtained in (*a*). **1**

(3)

[Turn over

DO NOT
WRITE IN
THIS
MARGIN

Marks

3. All enzymes are globular proteins.

(*a*) What term is used to describe proteins which are **not** globular?

1

(*b*) Catalase is an enzyme, contained in potatoes.
A student was studying the effect of varying pH on the activity of catalase.
The following apparatus was set up and left for 3 minutes.

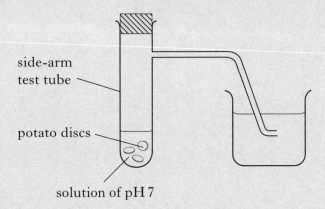

side-arm
test tube

potato discs

solution of pH 7

(i) What must be added to the side-arm test tube to study the enzyme activity at this pH?

1

(ii) Describe how the enzyme activity at this pH can be measured.

1

(3)

Marks

4. (*a*) Nuclear reactions can be carried out by scientists. For example, lawrencium–257 has been made by bombarding californium–252 with atoms of an isotope of a lighter element. Each successful collision was accompanied by the release of six neutrons.

Write a nuclear equation for this reaction.

1

(*b*) An example of a nuclear reaction which happens in nature is:

$$_{6}^{12}C + _{2}^{4}He \rightarrow _{8}^{16}O$$

Where do reactions of this type take place all the time?

1

(2)

[Turn over

5. A group of students carried out experiments to find the enthalpy of combustion of butan-1-ol (C_4H_9OH).

   Their results are shown on the graph.

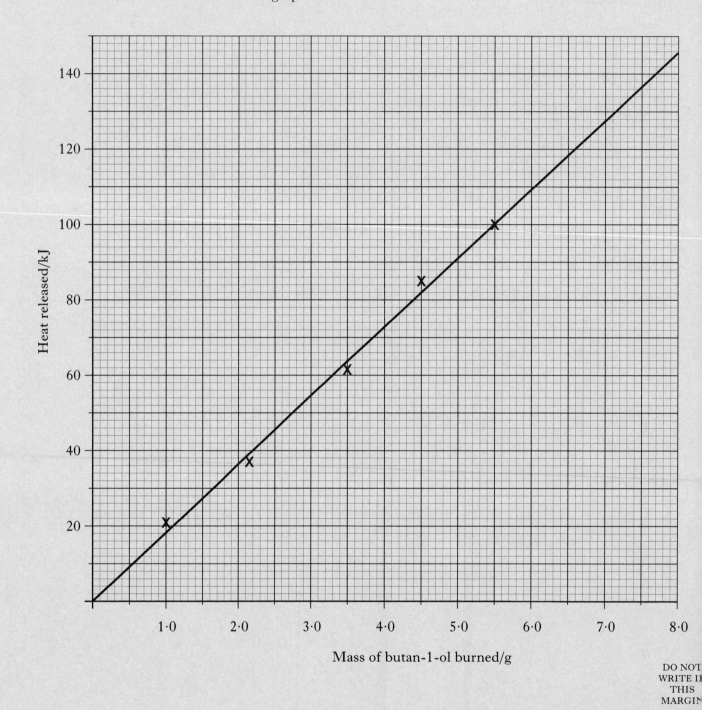

(a) Use the graph to find the heat released by burning 0·10 mol of butan-1-ol.

DO NOT
WRITE IN
THIS
MARGIN

Marks

1

Marks

5. **(continued)**

(b) Draw a labelled diagram of the assembled apparatus the students could have used to carry out the experiments.

1

(c) (i) **In another experiment** a group of students found that 0·10 mol of butan-1-ol released 143 kJ on burning.

Use this value to calculate the enthalpy of combustion of butan-1-ol.

1

(ii) The enthalpies of combustion of methanol, ethanol and propan-1-ol are given in the data booklet.

Use these values to predict the enthalpy of combustion of butan-1-ol.

1

(iii) In addition to heat loss, give another reason to explain why the experimental value for the enthalpy of combustion of butan-1-ol is significantly lower than the value given in data books.

1

(5)

[Turn over

Marks

6. Methanoic acid, HCOOH, can break down to carbon monoxide and water by two different reactions, **A** and **B**.

Reaction A (catalysed)

$$HCOOH(aq) \ + \ H^+(aq) \ \longrightarrow \ CO(g) \ + \ H_2O\ (\ell) \ + \ H^+(aq)$$

Reaction B (uncatalysed)

$$HCOOH(aq) \ \xrightarrow{\text{heat}} \ CO(g) \ + \ H_2O\ (\ell)$$

(a) (i) What is the evidence in the equation for Reaction **A** that the $H^+(aq)$ ion acts as a catalyst?

1

(ii) Explain whether Reaction **A** is an example of heterogeneous or homogeneous catalysis.

1

(b) The energy diagram for the **catalysed** reaction is:

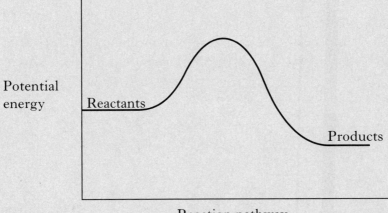

Draw a line on the diagram to show the reaction pathway for the **uncatalysed** reaction.

1

(3)

Marks

7. Diphosphine, P_2H_4, is a hydride of phosphorus. All of the covalent bonds in diphosphine molecules are non-polar because the elements present have the same electronegativity.

(*a*) What is meant by the term "electronegativity"?

1

(*b*) The balanced equation for the complete combustion of diphosphine is:

$$2P_2H_4(g) \quad + \quad 7O_2(g) \quad \rightarrow \quad P_4O_{10}(s) \quad + \quad 4H_2O \, (\ell)$$

What volume of oxygen would be required for the complete combustion of $10 \, cm^3$ of diphosphine?

1

(*c*) Calculate the volume occupied by $0 \cdot 330 \, g$ of diphosphine.

(Take the molar volume to be $24 \cdot 0$ litres mol^{-1}.)

(Show your working clearly.)

1

(3)

[Turn over

DO NOT
WRITE
THIS
MARGIN

Marks

8. The balanced equation for a reaction at equilibrium is:

$$aA \ + \ bB \ \rightleftharpoons \ cC \ + \ dD$$

(*a*) For this reaction, the equilibrium constant, **K**, can be defined as:

$$K = \frac{[C]^c [D]^d}{[A]^a [B]^b}$$

where **[A]** represents the concentration of **A**, etc and **a** represents the number of moles of **A**, etc.

   (i) Write down the expression for the equilibrium constant for the following equilibrium.

$$N_2(g) \ + \ 3H_2(g) \ \rightleftharpoons \ 2NH_3(g)$$

1

   (ii) What will happen to the position of an equilibrium if the reaction is carried out over a catalyst?

1

(*b*) In industry, the reaction of nitrogen with hydrogen to produce ammonia by the Haber Process does **not** attain equilibrium.

Give **one** feature of the operating conditions which leads to the Haber Process not reaching equilibrium.

1

(3)

Marks

9. Two reactions of propanoic acid are shown.

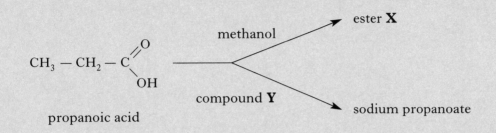

   propanoic acid

(*a*) Draw a structural formula for ester **X**.

1

(*b*) (i) Give a name for compound **Y**, which reacts with propanoic acid to form sodium propanoate.

1

    (ii) Explain why solutions of sodium propanoate are alkaline.

2

(4)

[Turn over

Marks

10. In 1996, the scientists Robert Curl, Harold Kroto and Richard Smalley won the Nobel Prize in Chemistry for their contribution to the discovery of new forms of carbon called fullerenes.

(a) In what way does the structure of fullerenes differ from the other forms of carbon, diamond and graphite?

1

(b) One form of fullerene, C_{60}, forms a superconducting crystalline compound with potassium.

Its formula can be represented as K_3C_{60}.

A sample of this compound was found to contain 2·88 g of carbon.

   (i) Calculate the number of moles of fullerene used to make this compound.

1

   (ii) Calculate the mass of potassium, in grams, in the sample.

1

(3)

Marks

11. Peeled apples turn brown due to the reactions of compounds called phenols.

The first two steps in the reaction of one phenol, **A**, are:

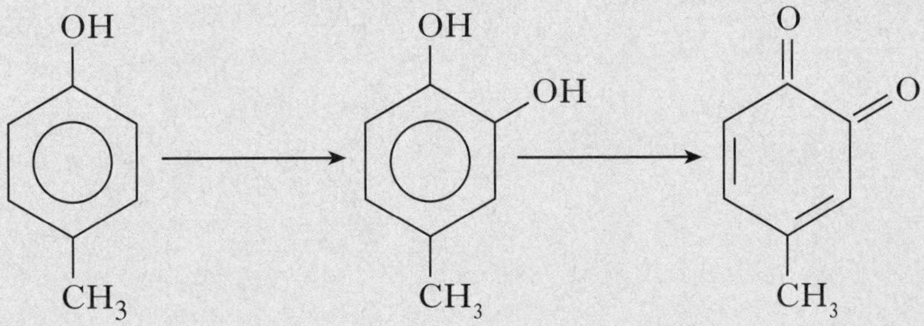

(a) The same type of reaction takes place in both steps.

Give the name of this type of reaction.

1

(b) The molecular formula for compound **A** can be written as C_7H_xO.

What is the value of x?

1

(c) An enzyme called phenolase, present in apples, acts as a catalyst during the browning of apples. It has been discovered that covering a slice of apple with lemon juice stops it from going brown.

Suggest a reason for this.

1

(3)

[Turn over

Marks

12. Some rockets have a propellant system which combines dinitrogen tetroxide with methylhydrazine.

$$5N_2O_4 \;+\; 4CH_3NHNH_2 \;\rightarrow\; xN_2 \;+\; yH_2O \;+\; zCO_2$$

(*a*) State the values of *x*, *y* and *z* required to balance the above equation.

1

(*b*) Draw the full structural formula for methylhydrazine.

1

(*c*) Methylhydrazine burns according to the following equation.

$$CH_3NHNH_2(\ell) + 2\tfrac{1}{2}O_2(g) \rightarrow CO_2(g) + 3H_2O(\ell) + N_2(g) \qquad \Delta H = \pm 1\,305\,kJ\,mol^{\pm1}$$

Use this information, together with information from page 9 of the data booklet, to calculate the enthalpy change for the following reaction.

$$C(s) \;+\; N_2(g) \;+\; 3H_2(g) \;\rightarrow\; CH_3NHNH_2(\ell)$$

(Show your working clearly.)

3

(5)

Marks

13. Ionisation energies provide information about the structure of atoms.

(*a*) Write the equation, showing state symbols, for the first ionisation energy of sodium.

1

(*b*) Calculate the number of electrons lost when one mole of boron atoms is converted into one mole of boron ions with a charge of 3+.

1

(2)

[Turn over

DO NO
WRITE
THIS
MARG

Marks

14. Alkanols can be prepared by the reaction of carbonyl compounds with methyl magnesium bromide. The reaction takes place in two stages.

Stage 1

Methyl magnesium bromide reacts with methanal in an addition reaction across the carbonyl group.

$$\begin{array}{c} H \\ \diagdown \\ \diagup \\ H \end{array} C=O \quad + \quad H-\underset{\underset{H}{|}}{\overset{\overset{H}{|}}{C}}-MgBr \quad \longrightarrow \quad H-\underset{\underset{H}{|}}{\overset{\overset{H}{|}}{C}}-\underset{\underset{H}{|}}{\overset{\overset{H}{|}}{C}}-O-MgBr$$

methanal   methyl magnesium
bromide

Stage 2

Reaction of the product with water produces ethanol.

$$H-\underset{\underset{H}{|}}{\overset{\overset{H}{|}}{C}}-\underset{\underset{H}{|}}{\overset{\overset{H}{|}}{C}}-O-MgBr \quad + \quad H_2O \quad \longrightarrow \quad H-\underset{\underset{H}{|}}{\overset{\overset{H}{|}}{C}}-\underset{\underset{H}{|}}{\overset{\overset{H}{|}}{C}}-OH \quad + \quad MgBrOH$$

ethanol

(*a*)   (i)   Suggest a name for the type of reaction which takes place in Stage 2.

1

(ii)   Draw a structural formula for the product if propanone had been used in place of methanal in this reaction.

1

Marks

14. **(*a*) (continued)**

(iii) A reaction in which 5·01 g of methanal was used yielded 5·75 g of ethanol. Calculate the percentage yield.

2

(*b*) State an important industrial use for methanal.

1

(5)

[Turn over

DO NO
WRITE
THIS
MARG

Marks

15. Vitamin C, $C_6H_8O_6$, is a powerful reducing agent. The concentration of vitamin C in a solution can be found by titrating it with a standard solution of iodine, using starch as an indicator. The equation for the reaction is:

$$C_6H_8O_6(aq) \quad + \quad I_2(aq) \quad \rightarrow \quad C_6H_6O_6(aq) \quad + \quad 2H^+(aq) \quad + \quad 2I^-(aq)$$

(*a*) Write an ion-electron equation for the reduction half-reaction.

1

(*b*) A work card gave the following instructions as part of an investigation into the vitamin C content of a tablet. Some instructions have been omitted.

ESTIMATION OF VITAMIN C

1. Add a vitamin C tablet to about $50\,cm^3$ of de-ionised water in a small beaker and stir to dissolve.

2. Transfer quantitatively to a $250\,cm^3$ standard flask.

3.

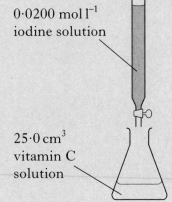

$0.0200\,mol\,l^{-1}$ iodine solution

$25.0\,cm^3$ vitamin C solution

(i) To "transfer quantitatively" means that **all** of the vitamin C must be transferred into the standard flask.

Describe how this is carried out in practice.

1

DO NOT
WRITE IN
THIS
MARGIN

Marks

15. **(*b*) (continued)**

   (ii) What colour change indicates that the end-point of the titration has been reached?

1

(*c*) In one investigation, it was found that an average of $29 \cdot 5 \, \text{cm}^3$ of $0 \cdot 02 \, \text{mol} \, \text{l}^{-1}$ iodine solution was required to react completely with $25 \cdot 0 \, \text{cm}^3$ of vitamin C solution.

Use this result to calculate the mass, in grams, of vitamin C present in each tablet.

3

(6)

[Turn over

Marks

16. Perfumes normally contain three groups of components called the **top note**, the **middle note** and the **end note**.

(a) The **top note** components of a perfume form vapours most easily. Two compounds found in **top note** components are:

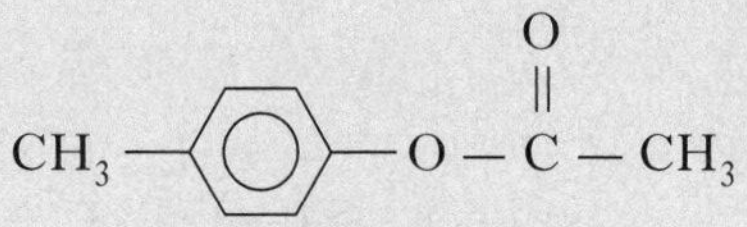

$$CH_3 - \langle\bigcirc\rangle - O - \overset{\overset{\textstyle O}{\|}}{C} - CH_3$$

p-cresyl acetate

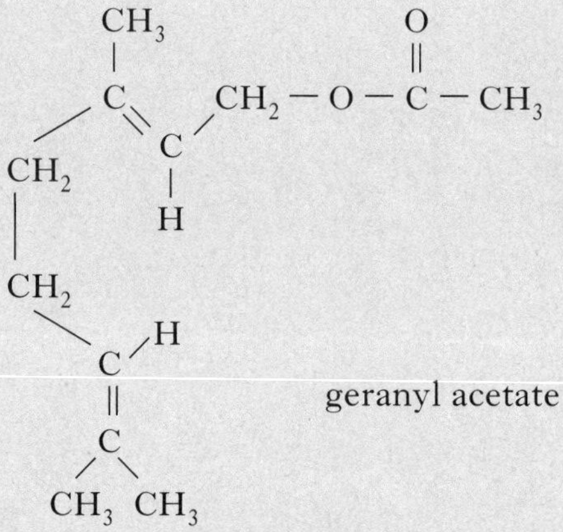

geranyl acetate

(i) With reference to the structure of these compounds, why are they likely to have pleasant smells?

1

(ii) Describe a chemical test which would distinguish between these two compounds and give the result of the test.

1

Marks

16. **(continued)**

(b) The **middle note** compounds form vapours less readily than the **top note** compounds. A typical compound of the **middle note** is:

2-phenylethanol

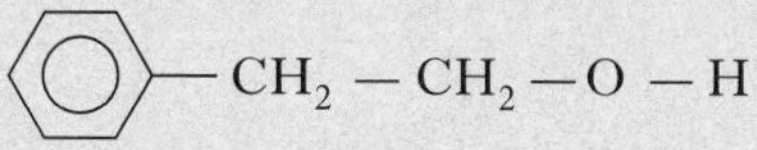

$$\langle\bigcirc\rangle - CH_2 - CH_2 - O - H$$

Due to hydrogen bonding 2-phenylethanol forms a vapour less readily than *p*-cresyl acetate.

In the box above, draw another molecule of 2-phenylethanol and use a dotted line to show where a hydrogen bond exists between the two molecules.

1

(c) The **end note** of a perfume has a long lasting odour which stays with the user. An example of an **end note** compound is:

civetone

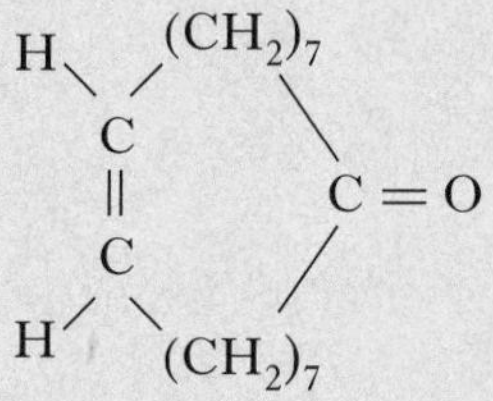

$$
\begin{array}{c}
H \diagdown \quad \diagup (CH_2)_7 \\
C \\
\| \qquad\qquad C = O \\
C \\
H \diagup \quad \diagdown (CH_2)_7
\end{array}
$$

Draw the structure of the alcohol which would be formed by the reduction of civetone.

1

(4)

[Turn over for Question 17 on *Page thirty-two*

DO NC
WRITE
THIS
MARGI

Marks

17. Chlorine can be manufactured by different industrial processes.

(*a*) In the Castner-Kellner cell, chlorine is made by the electrolysis of brine (sodium chloride solution).

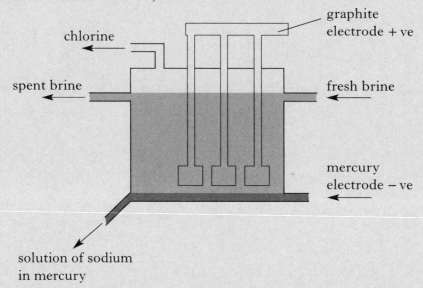

(i) Why is graphite able to conduct electricity?

1

(ii) In the above process, the solution of sodium in mercury is treated with water to give two useful products.

Name these **two** products.

1

(*b*) Chlorine was once made from hydrogen chloride and air by the Deacon Process.

$$4HCl(g) \quad + \quad O_2(g) \quad \rightarrow \quad 2Cl_2(g) \quad + \quad 2H_2O(g)$$

Suggest **one** reason why the Deacon Process was less economical to operate than the Castner-Kellner cell.

1

(3)

[END OF QUESTION PAPER]

2001 HIGHER

FOR OFFICIAL USE

Total
Section B

X012/301

NATIONAL
QUALIFICATIONS
2001

THURSDAY, 24 MAY
9.00 AM – 11.30 AM

CHEMISTRY
HIGHER

Fill in these boxes and read what is printed below.

Full name of centre

Town

Forename(s)

Surname

Date of birth
Day Month Year   Scottish candidate number   Number of seat

Reference may be made to the Chemistry Higher and Advanced Higher Data Booklet (1999 edition).

SECTION A—Part 1 Questions 1–30 and Part 2 Questions 31–35

Instructions for completion of **Part 1** and **Part 2** are given on pages two and seven respectively.

SECTION B

1   All questions should be attempted.

2   The questions may be answered in any order but all answers are to be written in the spaces provided in this answer book, and must be written clearly and legibly in ink.

3   Rough work, if any should be necessary, should be written in this book and then scored through when the fair copy has been written.

4   Additional space for answers and rough work will be found at the end of the book. If further space is required, supplementary sheets may be obtained from the invigilator and should be inserted inside the **front** cover of this book.

5   The size of the space provided for an answer should not be taken as an indication of how much to write. It is not necessary to use all the space.

6   Before leaving the examination room you must give this book to the invigilator. If you do not, you may lose all the marks for this paper.

SCOTTISH
QUALIFICATIONS
AUTHORITY

SECTION A

PART 1

Check that the answer sheet provided is for Chemistry Higher (Section A).

Fill in the details required on the answer sheet.

In questions 1 to 30 of this part of the paper, an answer is given by indicating the choice A, B, C or D by a stroke made in INK in the appropriate place in Part 1 of the answer sheet—see the sample question below.

For each question there is only ONE correct answer.

Rough working, if required, should be done only on this question paper, or on the rough working sheet provided—**not** on the answer sheet.

At the end of the examination the answer sheet for Section A **must** be placed **inside** this answer book.

This part of the paper is worth 30 marks.

SAMPLE QUESTION

To show that the ink in a ball-pen consists of a mixture of dyes, the method of separation would be

        A fractional distillation

        B chromatography

        C fractional crystallisation

        D filtration.

The correct answer is B—chromatography. A **heavy** vertical line should be drawn joining the two dots in the appropriate box in the column headed **B** as shown **in the example on the answer sheet**.

If, after you have recorded your answer, you decide that you have made an error and wish to make a change, you should cancel the original answer and put a vertical stroke in the box you now consider to be correct. Thus, if you want to change an answer **D** to an answer **B**, your answer sheet would look like this:

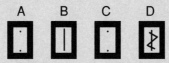

If you want to change back to an answer which has already been scored out, you should **enter a tick (✓)** to the RIGHT of the box of your choice, thus:

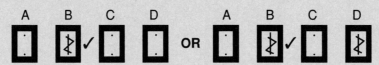

1. A negatively charged particle with electronic configuration 2, 8 could be

    A a fluoride ion

    B a sodium atom

    C an aluminium ion

    D a neon atom.

2. Which gas would dissolve in water to form an alkali?

    A HBr

    B NH_3

    C CO_2

    D CH_4

3. $20\,cm^3$ of $0.3\,mol\,l^{-1}$ sodium hydroxide solution can be exactly neutralised by

    A $20\,cm^3$ of $0.3\,mol\,l^{-1}$ sulphuric acid

    B $20\,cm^3$ of $0.6\,mol\,l^{-1}$ sulphuric acid

    C $10\,cm^3$ of $0.6\,mol\,l^{-1}$ sulphuric acid

    D $10\,cm^3$ of $0.3\,mol\,l^{-1}$ sulphuric acid.

4. A mixture of sodium bromide and sodium sulphate is known to contain 5 mol of sodium and 2 mol of bromide ions.

    How many moles of sulphate ions are present?

    A 1·5

    B 2·0

    C 2·5

    D 3·0

5. Excess marble chips (calcium carbonate) were added to $25\,cm^3$ of hydrochloric acid, concentration $2\,mol\,l^{-1}$.

    Which measurement, taken at regular intervals and plotted against time, would give the graph shown below?

    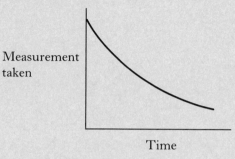

    A Temperature

    B Volume of gas produced

    C pH of solution

    D Mass of the beaker and contents

6. The following potential energy diagram is for an uncatalysed reaction.

    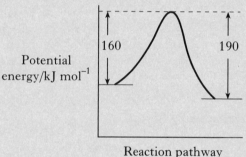

    When a catalyst is used the activation energy of the forward reaction is reduced to $35\,kJ\,mol^{-1}$.

    What is the activation energy of the catalysed reverse reaction, in $kJ\,mol^{-1}$?

    A   35

    B   65

    C 125

    D 155

7. The enthalpy of neutralisation in an acid/alkali reaction is **always** the energy released in

    A the neutralisation of one mole of acid

    B the neutralisation of one mole of alkali

    C the formation of one mole of water

    D the formation of one mole of salt.

    [Turn over

8. Which entry in the table shows the trends in the electronegativity values of the elements in the Periodic Table?

	Across a period	Down a group
A	decrease	decrease
B	decrease	increase
C	increase	decrease
D	increase	increase

9. Which type of structure is found in a fullerene?

A Ionic lattice

B Metallic lattice

C Covalent network

D Covalent molecular

10. Which type of bonding can be described as intermolecular?

A Covalent bonding

B Hydrogen bonding

C Ionic bonding

D Metallic bonding

11. An element melts at about room temperature and forms an oxide which reacts with water to form a solution with a pH less than 7.

Which statement is most likely to be true?

A The element conducts electricity.

B The oxide contains covalent bonds.

C The oxide has a high melting point.

D The element has a covalent network structure.

12. Which gas occupies the largest volume?

(Assume all measurements are made at the same temperature and pressure.)

A 0·32 g of oxygen

B 0·44 g of carbon dioxide

C 0·20 g of hydrogen

D 0·80 g of argon

13. In which reaction is the volume of products less than the volume of reactants?

A $CH_4(g) + 2O_2(g) \rightarrow CO_2(g) + 2H_2O(g)$

B $2NH_3(g) \rightarrow N_2(g) + 3H_2(g)$

C $H_2(g) + Cl_2(g) \rightarrow 2HCl(g)$

D $2CO(g) + O_2(g) \rightarrow 2CO_2(g)$

14. The Avogadro Constant is the same as the number of

A molecules in 16 g of oxygen

B electrons in 1 g of hydrogen

C atoms in 24 g of carbon

D ions in 1 litre of sodium chloride solution, concentration 1 $mol\,l^{-1}$.

15. Biogas is produced under anaerobic conditions by the fermentation of biological materials.

What is the main constituent of biogas?

A Butane

B Ethane

C Methane

D Propane

16. Which equation represents a reaction which takes place during reforming?

A $C_6H_{14} \rightarrow C_6H_6 + 4H_2$

B $C_4H_8 + H_2 \rightarrow C_4H_{10}$

C $C_2H_5OH \rightarrow C_2H_4 + H_2O$

D $C_8H_{18} \rightarrow C_4H_{10} + C_4H_8$

17. Which compound has isomeric forms?

A Methanol

B Propane

C C_2HCl_3

D $C_2H_4Cl_2$

18. What is the product when one mole of ethyne reacts with one mole of chlorine?

A 1,1-dichloroethene

B 1,1-dichloroethane

C 1,2-dichloroethene

D 1,2-dichloroethane

19. Which structural formula represents a primary alcohol?

A
$$CH_3 - CH_2 - CH_2 - \underset{\underset{OH}{|}}{\overset{\overset{H}{|}}{C}} - CH_3$$

B
$$CH_3 - CH_2 - \underset{\underset{OH}{|}}{\overset{\overset{H}{|}}{C}} - CH_2 - CH_3$$

C
$$CH_3 - \underset{\underset{OH}{|}}{\overset{\overset{CH_3}{|}}{C}} - CH_2 - CH_3$$

D
$$CH_3 - \underset{\underset{CH_3}{|}}{\overset{\overset{CH_3}{|}}{C}} - CH_2 - OH$$

20. An ester has the structural formula:

$$CH_3 - CH_2 - \overset{\overset{O}{\|}}{C} - O - \underset{\underset{CH_3}{|}}{\overset{\overset{CH_3}{|}}{C}} - H$$

On hydrolysis, the ester would produce

A ethanoic acid and propan-1-ol

B ethanoic acid and propan-2-ol

C propanoic acid and propan-1-ol

D propanoic acid and propan-2-ol.

21. The dehydration of butan-2-ol can produce two isomeric alkenes, but-1-ene and but-2-ene.

Which alkanol can similarly produce, on dehydration, a pair of isomeric alkenes?

A Propan-2-ol

B Pentan-3-ol

C Hexan-3-ol

D Heptan-4-ol

22. Ozone has an important role in the upper atmosphere because it

A reflects ultraviolet radiation

B reflects certain CFCs

C absorbs ultraviolet radiation

D absorbs certain CFCs.

23. Which statement can be applied to polymeric esters?

A They are used for flavourings, perfumes and solvents.

B They are condensation polymers made by the linking up of amino acids.

C They are manufactured for use as textile fabrics and resins.

D They are cross-linked addition polymers.

24. In α-amino acids the amino group is on the carbon atom adjacent to the acid group.

Which of the following is an α-amino acid?

A
$$CH_3 - \underset{\underset{CH_2 - NH_2}{|}}{CH} - COOH$$

B
$$\underset{\underset{SH}{|}}{CH_2} - \underset{\underset{NH_2}{|}}{CH} - COOH$$

C
NH_2 (top) COOH (bottom, para)

D.
NH_2 (top) COOH (ortho)

[Turn over

25. Which compound is **not** a raw material in the chemical industry?

    A   Benzene

    B   Water

    C   Iron oxide

    D   Sodium chloride

26. Which of the following is produced by a batch process?

    A   Sulphuric acid from sulphur and oxygen

    B   Aspirin from salicylic acid

    C   Iron from iron ore

    D   Ammonia from nitrogen and hydrogen

27.

$$Cl_2(g) + H_2O(\ell) \rightleftharpoons Cl^-(aq) + ClO^-(aq) + 2H^+(aq)$$

    The addition of which substance would move the above equilibrium to the right?

    A   Hydrogen

    B   Hydrogen chloride

    C   Sodium chloride

    D   Sodium hydroxide

28. The concentration of $H^+(aq)$ ions in a solution is 1×10^{-4} mol l^{-1}.

    What is the concentration of $OH^-(aq)$ ions, in mol l^{-1}?

    A 1×10^{-4}

    B 1×10^{-7}

    C 1×10^{-10}

    D 1×10^{-14}

29. Equal volumes of solutions of ethanoic acid and hydrochloric acid, of equal concentrations, are compared.

    In which of the following cases does the ethanoic acid give the higher value?

    A   pH of solution

    B   Conductivity of solution

    C   Rate of reaction with magnesium

    D   Volume of sodium hydroxide solution neutralised

30. Two 1 g samples of radium and radium oxide both contain the same radioisotope of radium. The intensity of radiation and half-life of the radioisotope in each sample are compared.

    Which entry in the table is a correct comparison?

	Intensity of radiation	Half-life
A	same	different
B	same	same
C	different	same
D	different	different

SECTION A

PART 2

In questions 31 to 35 of this part of the paper, an answer is given by circling the appropriate letter (or letters) in the answer grids provided on Part 2 of the answer sheet.

In some questions, two letters are required for full marks.

If more than the correct number of answers is given, marks may be deducted.

In some cases the number of correct responses is NOT identified in the question.

This part of the paper is worth 10 marks.

SAMPLE QUESTION

A CH_4	B H_2	C CO_2
D CO	E C_2H_6	F N_2

(a)   Identify the diatomic **compound(s)**.

A	B	C
(D)	E	F

The one correct answer to part (a) is D. This should be circled.

(b)   Identify the **two** substances which burn to produce **both** carbon dioxide **and** water.

(A)	B	C
D	(E)	F

As indicated in this question, there are **two** correct answers to part (b). These are A and E.

Both answers are circled.

(c)   Identify the substance(s) which can **not** be used as a fuel.

A	B	(C)
D	E	(F)

There are **two** correct answers to part (c). These are C and F.

Both answers are circled.

If, after you have recorded your answer, you decide that you have made an error and wish to make a change, you should cancel the original answer and circle the answer you now consider to be correct. Thus, in part (a), if you want to change an answer **D** to an answer **A**, your answer sheet would look like this:

(A)	B	C
D̶	E	F

If you want to change back to an answer which has already been scored out, you should enter a tick (✓) in the box of the answer of your choice, thus:

A̶	B	C
✓ D̶	E	F

31. The properties of substances depend on their structures and bonding.

A	B	C
hydrogen	phosphorus	sodium

D	E	F
lithium hydroxide	hydrogen fluoride	hydrogen iodide

(*a*)   Identify the substance with hydrogen bonding between the molecules.

(*b*)   Identify the **two** substances with pure covalent bonding in the molecules.

32. The grid shows the possible effect of temperature change on reaction rate.

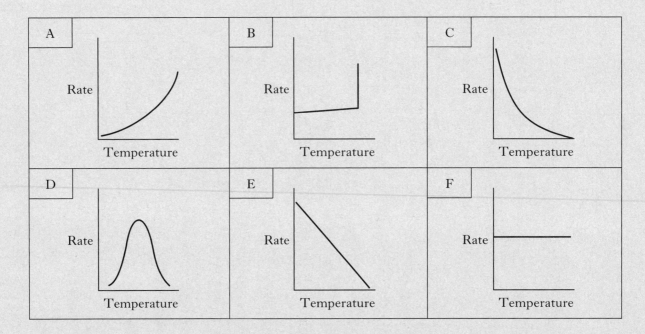

Identify the graph which shows how the rate of reaction varies with temperature in

(*a*)   the decomposition of hydrogen peroxide solution using catalase, an enzyme found in potatoes,

(*b*)   the radioactive decay of phosphorus-32.

33. Propan-2-ol can be prepared from propane as follows.

$$CH_3 - CH_2 - CH_3 \xrightarrow{\text{Step 1}} CH_3 - CH = CH_2 \xrightarrow{\text{Step 2}} CH_3 - \underset{\underset{OH}{|}}{CH} - CH_3$$

A		B		C	
	condensation		cracking		dehydration

D		E		F	
	hydration		hydrolysis		oxidation

(a) Identify the name of the type of reaction taking place at Step 1.

(b) Identify the name of the type of reaction taking place at Step 2.

34. Identify the statement(s) which can be applied to the role of a catalyst in a reversible reaction.

A	It decreases the enthalpy change for the reaction.
B	It decreases the time required for equilibrium to be established.
C	It alters the equilibrium position.
D	It lowers the activation energy of the backward reaction.
E	It increases the rate of the forward reaction more than the backward reaction.

[Turn over

35. Sodium sulphite is a salt of sulphurous acid, a weak acid.

Identify the statement(s) which can be applied to sodium sulphite.

You may wish to refer to the data booklet.

A	It can be prepared by a precipitation reaction.
B	It can be prepared by the reaction of sulphurous acid with sodium carbonate.
C	In solution, the pH is lower than a solution of sodium sulphate.
D	In redox reactions in solution, the sulphite ion acts as a reducing agent.
E	In redox reactions in solution, the sodium ions are oxidised.

Candidates are reminded that the answer sheet MUST be returned INSIDE this answer book.

Marks

SECTION B

1. Technetium-99, which has a long half-life, is produced as a radioactive waste product in nuclear reactors. One way of reducing the danger of this isotope is to change it into technetium-100 by bombardment with particles, as shown by the nuclear equation.

$$^{99}_{43}\text{Tc} \ + \ \textbf{X} \ \rightarrow \ ^{100}_{43}\text{Tc}$$

(*a*) Identify particle **X**.

1

(*b*) Technetium-100 decays by beta-emission.

Write a balanced nuclear equation for this reaction.

1

(*c*) Technetium-100 has a half-life of 16 s.

If a sample of technetium-100 is left for 48 s, what fraction of the sample would remain?

1

(3)

[Turn over

Marks

2. Steam reforming of coal produces a mixture of carbon monoxide and hydrogen.

(*a*) What name is given to this mixture of carbon monoxide and hydrogen?

1

(*b*) This mixture could be used to produce methane, as shown by the following equilibrium.

$$CO(g) \ + \ 3H_2(g) \ \rightleftharpoons \ CH_4(g) \ + \ H_2O(g) \qquad \Delta H = -206\,kJ\,mol^{-1}$$

Give **two** reasons why the yield of methane can be increased by cooling the reaction mixture from 400 °C to 80 °C.

2

(3)

Marks

3. The effect of temperature changes on reaction rate can be studied using the reaction between an organic acid solution and acidified potassium permanganate solution.

$$5(COOH)_2(aq) + 6H^+(aq) + 2MnO_4^-(aq) \longrightarrow 2Mn^{2+}(aq) + 10CO_2(g) + 8H_2O(\ell)$$

The apparatus required is shown in the diagram.

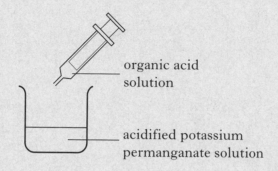

organic acid
solution

acidified potassium
permanganate solution

(a) Name the organic acid.

1

(b) Describe how the reaction time can be measured.

1

(c) The headings for a set of results are shown below.

Temperature of reaction/°C	Reaction time/s	Reaction rate/

Complete the headings by entering the correct unit in the **third** column.

1

(3)

[Turn over

Marks

4. A student heated a compound which gave off carbon dioxide and water vapour.

Lumps of calcium chloride were used to absorb the water vapour first, and the carbon dioxide was then collected **in such a way that its volume could be measured**.

(a) Complete the diagram below to show the absorption of water vapour and collection of carbon dioxide.

Label the diagram clearly.

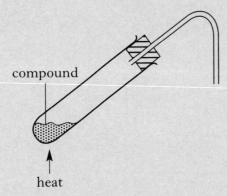

compound

heat

2

(b) The volume of carbon dioxide collected was $240 \, cm^3$.

Calculate the number of molecules in this volume.

(Take the molar volume of carbon dioxide to be 24 litres mol^{-1}.)

1

(3)

Marks

5. Vinyl acetate is the monomer for the preparation of polyvinylacetate (PVA) which is widely used in the building industry.

Vinyl acetate has the structural formula:

$$CH_3 - \overset{\overset{\textstyle O}{\|}}{C} - O - CH = CH_2$$

(a) Draw part of the structure of polyvinylacetate, showing **three** monomer units joined together.

1

(b) Vinyl acetate and hexane have the same relative formula mass.

Explain why you would expect vinyl acetate to have a higher boiling point than hexane.

2

(3)

[Turn over

DO NO
WRITE
THIS
MARG

Marks

6. Aluminium is extracted from bauxite. This ore contains aluminium oxide along with iron(III) oxide and other impurities. The process is shown in the flow diagram.

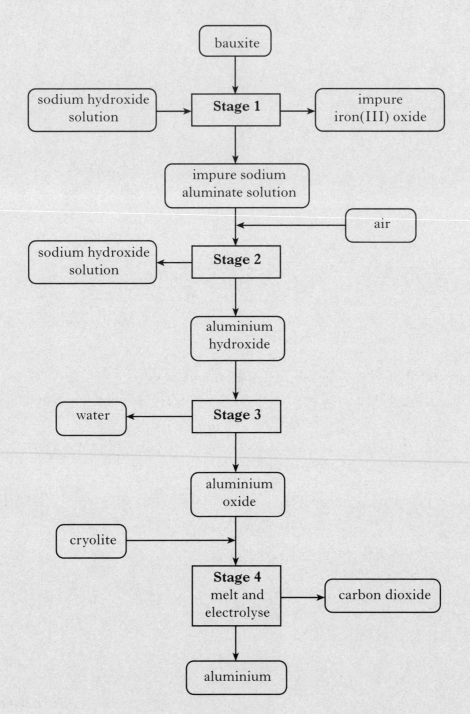

    (*a*) Add an arrow to the flow diagram to show how the process could be made more economical.

1

Marks

6. **(continued)**

(*b*) In **Stage 1** of the process, aluminium oxide reacts with sodium hydroxide solution.

State whether aluminium oxide is behaving as an acidic oxide or as a basic oxide in this reaction.

1

(*c*) What type of reaction takes place during **Stage 3**?

1

(*d*) During **Stage 4**, aluminium is manufactured in cells by the electrolysis of aluminium oxide dissolved in molten cryolite.

What mass of aluminium is produced each hour, if the current passing through the liquid is 180 000 A?

Show your working clearly.

3

(*e*) In **Stage 4**, the carbon blocks that are used as positive electrodes must be regularly replaced.

Suggest a reason for this.

1

(7)

Marks

7. Potassium hydroxide can be used in experiments to verify Hess's Law. The reactions concerned can be summarised as follows.

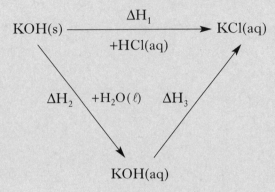

$$KOH(s) \xrightarrow[+HCl(aq)]{\Delta H_1} KCl(aq)$$

$$\Delta H_2 \quad +H_2O(\ell) \quad \Delta H_3$$

$$KOH(aq)$$

(*a*) State Hess's Law.

1

(*b*) Complete the list of measurements that would have to be made in order to calculate ΔH_2.

   (i) Mass of potassium hydroxide

   (ii)

   (iii)

   (iv)

1

(*c*) What solution must be added to the potassium hydroxide solution in order to calculate ΔH_3?

1

(3)

Marks

8. Calcium hydroxyapatite makes up 95% of tooth enamel.

(*a*) Tooth decay is caused when tooth enamel is attacked by acid in the mouth.

(i) One of the acids which attacks tooth enamel is 2-hydroxypropanoic acid, which has the molecular formula $C_3H_6O_3$.

Draw a structural formula for this acid.

1

(ii) Calcium hydroxyapatite reacts with acid in the mouth as shown by the following balanced equation.

$$Ca_{10}(PO_4)_6(OH)_2 \ + \ 8H^+ \ \longrightarrow \ 10Ca^{2+} \ + \ 2H_2O \ + \ 6HPO_4^{\,x-}$$
calcium hydroxyapatite

What is the value of x?

1

(iii) The pH of a solution in the mouth is 5.

What is the concentration of hydrogen ions, in mol l^{-1}, in this solution?

1

(*b*) Tooth enamel also contains a fibrous protein called collagen.

(i) Describe a difference between a fibrous and a globular protein.

1

(ii) Name the **four** elements present in all proteins.

1

(5)

Marks

9. (*a*) Kevlar and Nomex are examples of recently manufactured polymers. Their properties are different because they are made from different monomers.

The diamine monomer used to make Nomex is 1,3-diaminobenzene.

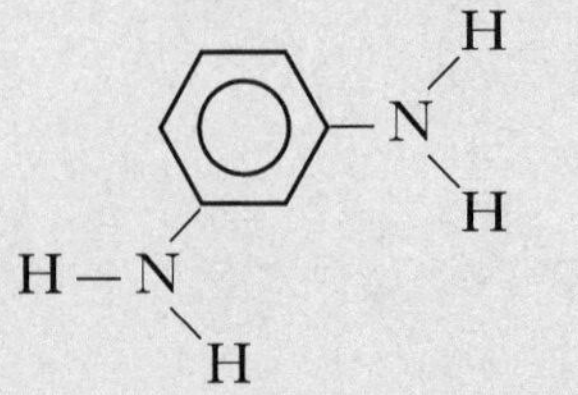

1,3-diaminobenzene

This reacts with the other monomer to form the repeating unit shown.

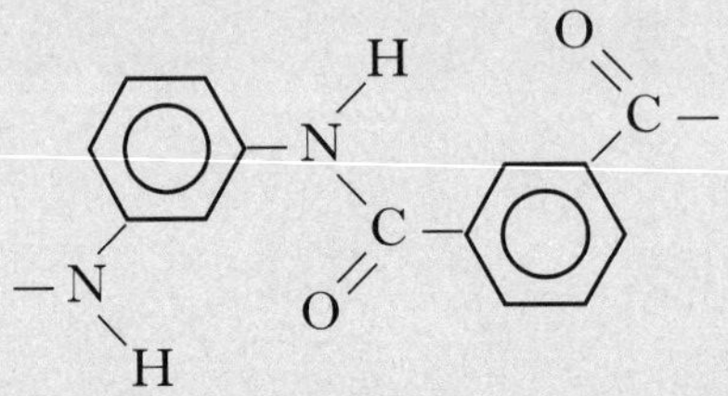

(i) Draw a structural formula for the other monomer.

1

(ii) The repeating unit in Kevlar is:

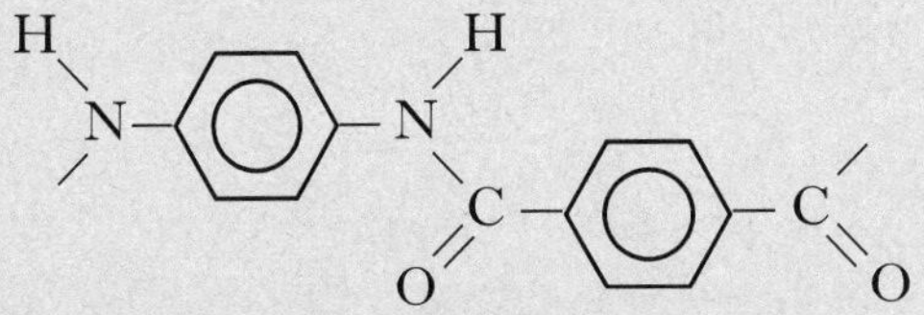

Name the diamine used to make Kevlar.

1

(*b*) Another recently manufactured polymer is polyvinylcarbazole.

Give the unusual property of polyvinylcarbazole which makes it suitable for use in photocopiers.

1

(3)

Marks

10. (*a*) Propanone and propanal both contain the same functional group.

    (i) Name this functional group.

1

    (ii) The diagram shows how to distinguish between propanone and propanal.

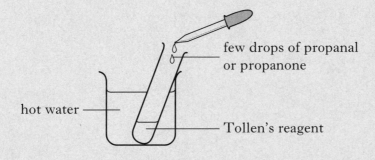

few drops of propanal
or propanone

hot water

Tollen's reagent

        Explain what is observed in the reaction between propanal and Tollen's reagent.

2

(*b*) The equation for the enthalpy of formation of propanone is:

$$3C(s) \quad + \quad 3H_2(g) \quad + \quad \tfrac{1}{2}O_2(g) \quad \longrightarrow \quad C_3H_6O(\ell)$$

Use the following information on enthalpies of combustion to calculate the enthalpy of formation of propanone.

$$C(s) \quad + \quad O_2(g) \quad \rightarrow \quad CO_2(g) \qquad \Delta H = -394 \text{ kJ mol}^{-1}$$
$$H_2(g) \quad + \quad \tfrac{1}{2}O_2(g) \quad \rightarrow \quad H_2O(\ell) \qquad \Delta H = -286 \text{ kJ mol}^{-1}$$
$$C_3H_6O(\ell) \quad + \quad 4O_2(g) \quad \rightarrow \quad 3CO_2(g) \quad + \quad 3H_2O(\ell) \quad \Delta H = -1804 \text{ kJ mol}^{-1}$$

Show your working clearly.

2

(5)

Marks

11. (*a*) Mordenite is a porous, crystalline material with a surface area of over $500\,m^2\,g^{-1}$.

It is used in an isomerisation reaction, part of a sequence which converts pentane into 2-methylbutane for blending into petrol.

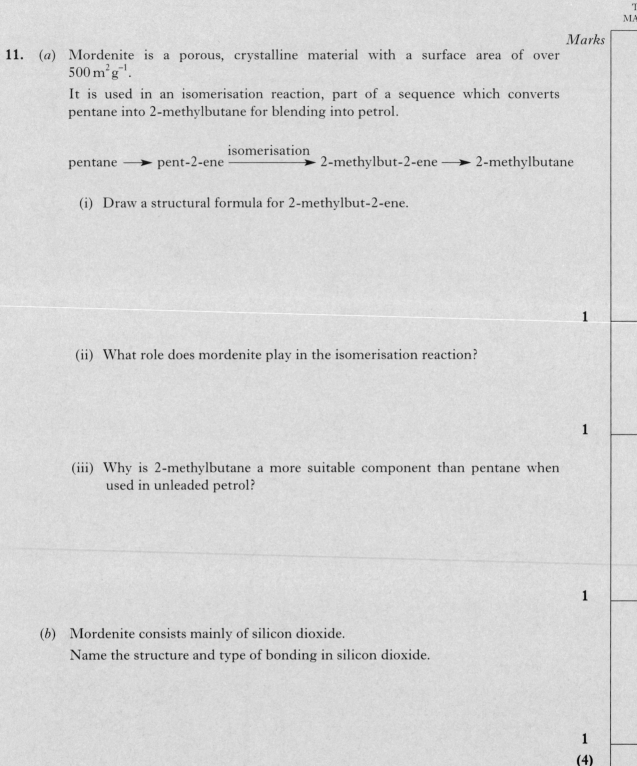

pentane $\longrightarrow$ pent-2-ene $\xrightarrow{\text{isomerisation}}$ 2-methylbut-2-ene $\longrightarrow$ 2-methylbutane

(i) Draw a structural formula for 2-methylbut-2-ene.

1

(ii) What role does mordenite play in the isomerisation reaction?

1

(iii) Why is 2-methylbutane a more suitable component than pentane when used in unleaded petrol?

1

(*b*) Mordenite consists mainly of silicon dioxide.

Name the structure and type of bonding in silicon dioxide.

1

(4)

Marks

12. On crossing the Periodic Table, there are trends in the sizes of atoms and ions.

(*a*) Why is the atomic size of chlorine less than that of sodium?

1

(*b*)

Ion	Ionic radius/pm
Si^{4+}	42
P^{3-}	198

Why is there a large increase in ionic radius on going from Si^{4+} to P^{3-}?

1

(2)

[Turn over

Marks

13. Ammonium chloride (NH_4Cl) is soluble in water.

   (*a*) How does the pH of a solution of ammonium chloride compare with the pH of water?

1

   (*b*) A student dissolved $10.0\,g$ of ammonium chloride in $200\,cm^3$ of water and found that the temperature of the solution fell from $23.2\,°C$ to $19.8\,°C$.

   Calculate the enthalpy of solution of ammonium chloride.

   Show your working clearly.

2

(3)

Marks

14. (*a*) Some carbon monoxide detectors contain crystals of hydrated palladium(II) chloride. These form palladium in a redox reaction if exposed to carbon monoxide.

$$CO(g) + PdCl_2.2H_2O(s) \longrightarrow CO_2(g) + Pd(s) + 2HCl(g) + H_2O(\ell)$$

Write the ion-electron equation for the reduction step in this reaction.

1

(*b*) Another type of detector uses an electrochemical method to detect carbon monoxide.

At the positive electrode:

$$CO(g) + H_2O(\ell) \longrightarrow CO_2(g) + 2H^+(aq) + 2e^-$$

At the negative electrode:

$$O_2(g) + 4H^+(aq) + 4e^- \longrightarrow 2H_2O(\ell)$$

Combine the two ion-electron equations to give the overall redox equation.

1

(2)

[Turn over

DO NO°
WRITE I
THIS
MARGI

Marks

15. Sugars, such as glucose, are often used as sweeteners in soft drinks.

The glucose content of a soft drink can be estimated by titration against a standardised solution of Benedict's solution. The copper(II) ions in Benedict's solution react with glucose as shown.

$$C_6H_{12}O_6(aq) + 2Cu^{2+}(aq) + 2H_2O(\ell) \longrightarrow Cu_2O(s) + 4H^+(aq) + C_6H_{12}O_7(aq)$$

(a) What change in the ratio of atoms present indicates that the conversion of glucose into the compound with molecular formula $C_6H_{12}O_7$ is an example of oxidation?

1

(b) In one experiment, $25 \cdot 0 \, \text{cm}^3$ volumes of a soft drink were titrated with Benedict's solution in which the concentration of copper(II) ions was $0 \cdot 500 \, \text{mol} \, \text{l}^{-1}$. The following results were obtained.

Titration	Volume of Benedict's solution/cm³
1	18·0
2	17·1
3	17·3

Average volume of Benedict's solution used $= 17 \cdot 2 \, \text{cm}^3$.

(i) Why was the first titration result not used in calculating the average volume of Benedict's solution?

1

Marks

15. **(*b*) (continued)**

    (ii) Calculate the concentration of glucose in the soft drink, in $mol\,l^{-1}$.

        Show your working clearly.

2

(*c*) In some soft drinks, sucrose is used instead of glucose.

Why can the sucrose concentration of a soft drink **not** be estimated by this method?

1

(5)

[Turn over

Marks

16. In experiments with four different gases, a syringe was held vertically as shown with the weight of the syringe piston applying a downward pressure on the gas. The times taken for $60\,cm^3$ of helium, methane, carbon dioxide and butane to escape through the pinhole were measured and the graph shows the results plotted against relative formula mass.

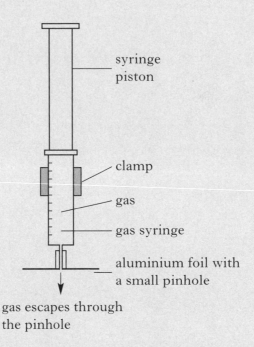

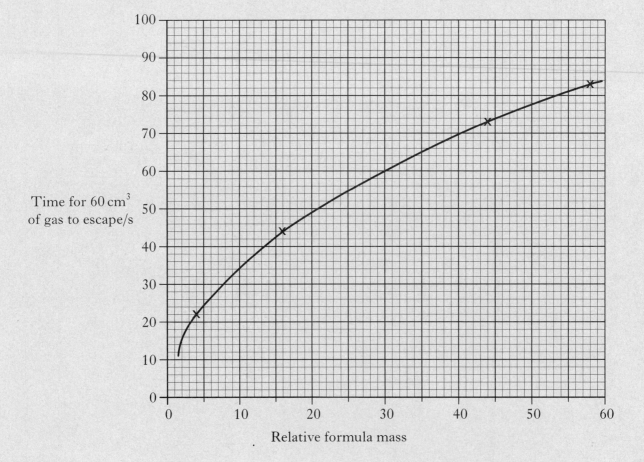

Marks

16. **(continued)**

(*a*) Calculate the average rate of escape from the syringe of $60 \, cm^3$ of methane, in $cm^3 \, s^{-1}$.

1

(*b*) Name a hydrocarbon gas which would take 56 s to escape.

1

(*c*) The error in a measurement decreases as the actual size of the measurement increases.

Suggest **one** way of reducing the error in each of the time measurements.

1

(3)

[Turn over for Question 17 on *Page thirty*

Marks

17. Biodiesel is a mixture of esters which can be made by heating rapeseed oil with methanol in the presence of a catalyst.

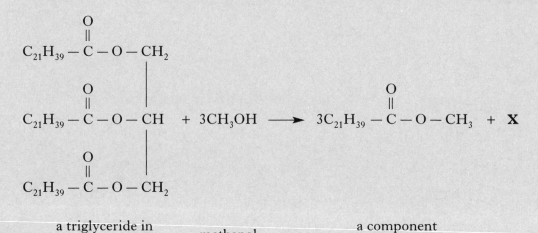

a triglyceride in rapeseed oil   methanol   a component of biodiesel

(a) Name compound **X**.

1

(b) A typical diesel molecule obtained from crude oil has the molecular formula $C_{16}H_{34}$ (hexadecane).

Other than the ester group, name a functional group present in biodiesel molecules which is **not** present in hexadecane.

1

(c) Vegetable oils like rapeseed oil are converted into fats for use in the food industry.

What name is given to this process?

1

(3)

[END OF QUESTION PAPER]

2002 HIGHER

FOR OFFICIAL USE

Total
Section B

X012/301

NATIONAL
QUALIFICATIONS
2002

TUESDAY, 4 JUNE
9.00 AM – 11.30 AM

CHEMISTRY
HIGHER

Fill in these boxes and read what is printed below.

Full name of centre

Town

Forename(s)

Surname

Date of birth
Day Month Year   Scottish candidate number   Number of seat

Reference may be made to the Chemistry Higher and Advanced Higher Data Booklet (1999 edition).

SECTION A—Part 1 Questions 1–30 and Part 2 Questions 31–35

Instructions for completion of **Part 1** and **Part 2** are given on pages two and eight respectively.

SECTION B

1   All questions should be attempted.

2   The questions may be answered in any order but all answers are to be written in the spaces provided in this answer book, and must be written clearly and legibly in ink.

3   Rough work, if any should be necessary, should be written in this book and then scored through when the fair copy has been written.

4   Additional space for answers and rough work will be found at the end of the book. If further space is required, supplementary sheets may be obtained from the invigilator and should be inserted inside the **front** cover of this book.

5   The size of the space provided for an answer should not be taken as an indication of how much to write. It is not necessary to use all the space.

6   Before leaving the examination room you must give this book to the invigilator. If you do not, you may lose all the marks for this paper.

SCOTTISH
QUALIFICATIONS
AUTHORITY

SECTION A

PART 1

1. Check that the answer sheet provided is for Chemistry Higher (Section A).

2. Fill in the details required on the answer sheet.

3. **In questions 1 to 30 of this part of the paper, an answer is given by indicating the choice A, B, C or D by a stroke made in INK in the appropriate place in Part 1 of the answer sheet—see the sample question below.**

4. **For each question there is only ONE correct answer.**

5. Rough working, if required, should be done only on this question paper, or on the rough working sheet provided—**not** on the answer sheet.

6. At the end of the examination the answer sheet for Section A **must** be placed **inside** the front cover of this answer book.

This part of the paper is worth 30 marks.

SAMPLE QUESTION

To show that the ink in a ball-pen consists of a mixture of dyes, the method of separation would be

        A   fractional distillation

        B   chromatography

        C   fractional crystallisation

        D   filtration.

The correct answer is B—chromatography. A **heavy** vertical line should be drawn joining the two dots in the appropriate box in the column headed **B** as shown **in the example on the answer sheet**.

If, after you have recorded your answer, you decide that you have made an error and wish to make a change, you should cancel the original answer and put a vertical stroke in the box you now consider to be correct. Thus, if you want to change an answer **D** to an answer **B**, your answer sheet would look like this:

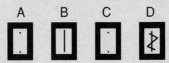

If you want to change back to an answer which has already been scored out, you should **enter a tick (✓)** to the RIGHT of the box of your choice, thus:

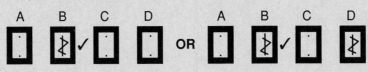

1. Which covalent gas dissolves in water to form an alkali?

   A   HCl

   B CH_4

   C SO_2

   D NH_3

2. When copper is added to a solution containing zinc nitrate and silver nitrate

   A   deposits of both zinc and silver form

   B   a deposit of zinc forms

   C   a deposit of silver forms

   D   no new deposit forms.

3. Hydrochloric acid reacts with magnesium according to the following equation.

   $$Mg(s) + 2H^+(aq) \rightarrow Mg^{2+}(aq) + H_2(g)$$

   What volume of $4\ mol\,l^{-1}$ hydrochloric acid reacts with $0 \cdot 1\ mol$ of magnesium?

   A $25\ cm^3$

   B $50\ cm^3$

   C $100\ cm^3$

   D $200\ cm^3$

4. Two identical samples of zinc were added to an excess of two solutions of sulphuric acid, concentrations $2\ mol\,l^{-1}$ and $1\ mol\,l^{-1}$ respectively.

   Which of the following would have been the same for the two samples?

   A   The total mass lost

   B   The total time for the reaction

   C   The initial reaction rate

   D   The average rate of evolution of gas

5.

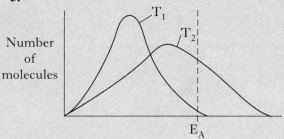

Kinetic energy of molecules

Which of the following is the correct interpretation of the above energy distribution diagram for a reaction as the temperature **decreases** from T_2 to T_1?

	Activation energy (E_A)	Number of successful collisions
A	remains the same	increases
B	decreases	decreases
C	decreases	increases
D	remains the same	decreases

6. The potential energy diagram for the reaction

   $$CO(g) + NO_2(g) \rightarrow CO_2(g) + NO(g)$$

   is shown.

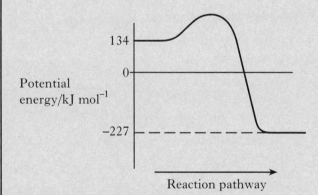

Reaction pathway

ΔH, in $kJ\ mol^{-1}$, for the forward reaction is

   A -361

   B -227

   C -93

   D $+361$.

[Turn over

7. Which type of bond is broken when ice is melted?

   A Ionic

   B Polar covalent

   C Hydrogen

   D Non-polar covalent

8. The shapes of some common molecules are shown below and each contains at least one polar bond.

   Which molecule is non-polar?

   A H — Cl

   B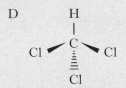

   C O = C = O

   D

11. The equation for the complete combustion of propane is:

   $$C_3H_8(g) + 5O_2(g) \rightarrow 3CO_2(g) + 4H_2O(\ell)$$

   $50\,cm^3$ of propane is mixed with $500\,cm^3$ of oxygen and the mixture is ignited.

   What is the volume of the resulting gas mixture?

   (All volumes are measured at the same temperature and pressure.)

   A $150\,cm^3$

   B $300\,cm^3$

   C $400\,cm^3$

   D $700\,cm^3$

12. It is now known that protons and neutrons are made up of smaller particles called quarks.

   Each proton and each neutron contains 3 quarks.

   What is the approximate number of quarks in 1 g of carbon-12?

   A 6×10^{23}

   B 9×10^{23}

   C $1 \cdot 8 \times 10^{24}$

   D $2 \cdot 16 \times 10^{25}$

9. A metal (melting point 843 °C, density $1 \cdot 54\,g\,cm^{-3}$) was obtained by electrolysis of its chloride (melting point 772 °C, density $2 \cdot 15\,g\,cm^{-3}$) at 780 °C.

   During the electrolysis, how would the metal occur?

   A As a solid on the surface of the electrolyte

   B As a liquid on the surface of the electrolyte

   C As a solid at the bottom of the electrolyte

   D As a liquid at the bottom of the electrolyte

13. Which pollutant, produced during internal combustion in a car engine, is **not** the result of incomplete combustion?

   A Nitrogen dioxide

   B Hydrocarbons

   C Carbon

   D Carbon monoxide

10. Which of the following contains the **largest** number of molecules?

   A 0·10 g of hydrogen gas

   B 0·17 g of ammonia gas

   C 0·32 g of methane gas

   D 0·35 g of chlorine gas

14. Which equation represents an industrial reforming process?

   A $CH_3(CH_2)_6CH_3 \rightarrow$
      $CH_3(CH_2)_4CH_3 + CH_2 = CH_2$

   B $CH_3(CH_2)_6CH_3 \rightarrow$
      $CH_3C(CH_3)_2CH_2CH(CH_3)_2$

   C $CH_3(CH_2)_6CH_2OH \rightarrow$
      $CH_3(CH_2)_5CH = CH_2 + H_2O$

   D $4CH_2 = CH_2 \rightarrow \ - (CH_2CH_2)_4 -$

15. Which of the following is an isomer of hexanal?

A   2-methylbutanal

B   3-methylpentan-2-one

C   2,2-dimethylbutan-1-ol

D   3-ethylpentanal

16. An ester is prepared from methanoic acid and ethanol.

Which of the following is the full structural formula for the ester produced?

A
```
    H   H        O
    |   |        ‖
H — C — C — O — C — H
    |   |
    H   H
```

B
```
    H   O        H
    |   ‖        |
H — C — C — O — C — H
    |            |
    H            H
```

C
```
    H   H        H
    |   |        |
H — C — C — O — C — H
    |   |        |
    H   H        H
```

D
```
    H   H   O
    |   |   ‖
H — C — C — C — O — H
    |   |
    H   H
```

17. Which statement about benzene is correct?

A   Benzene is an isomer of cyclohexane.

B   Benzene reacts with bromine solution as if it is unsaturated.

C   The ratio of carbon to hydrogen atoms in benzene is the same as in ethyne.

D   Benzene undergoes addition reactions more readily than hexene.

18. Which reaction can be classified as reduction?

A $CH_3CH_2OH \rightarrow CH_3COOH$

B $CH_3CH(OH)CH_3 \rightarrow CH_3COCH_3$

C $CH_3CH_2COCH_3 \rightarrow CH_3CH_2CH(OH)CH_3$

D $CH_3CH_2CHO \rightarrow CH_3CH_2COOH$

19. Part of a polymer molecule is represented below.

```
 CH₃  H    CH₃  H    CH₃  H    CH₃  H
  |   |     |   |     |   |     |   |
— C — C — C — C — C — C — C — C —
  |   |     |   |     |   |     |   |
  H   CH₃   H   CH₃   H   CH₃   H   CH₃
```

The monomer which gives rise to this polymer is

A   but-2-ene

B   but-1-ene

C   methylpropene

D   buta-1,3-diene.

20. Which mixture of gases is known as synthesis gas?

A   Methane and oxygen

B   Carbon monoxide and oxygen

C   Carbon dioxide and hydrogen

D   Carbon monoxide and hydrogen

21. Some recently developed polymers have unusual properties.

Which polymer is soluble in water?

A   Poly(ethyne)

B   Poly(ethenol)

C   Biopol

D   Kevlar

[Turn over

22. When two amino acids condense together, water is eliminated and a peptide link is formed.

Which of the following represents this process?

A

```
    H     R₁   ⌐O ̄ ̄ ̄ ̄ ̄H⌐     R₂    O
     \    |    ‖ ̄ ̄ ̄ ̄ ̄|      |    ‖
      N — C — C          ⌐ ̄N — C — C
     /    |     \        ||    |     \
    H     H     OH      H⌐    H      OH
```

B

```
    H     R₁   O              R₂    O
     \    |    ‖               |    ‖
      N — C — C - - - -H⌐ C — C
     /    |     \       \      |     \
    H     H     ⌐OH - - - -    N     OH
                              /  \
                             H    H
```

C

```
    H     R₁   O          H     R₂    O
     \    |    ‖           |     |    ‖
      N — C — C            N — C — C
     /    |     \         /      |     \
    H     H    ⌐OH     H⌐   H      OH
                └ ̄ ̄ ̄ ̄ ̄ ̄┘
```

D

```
    H     R₁   O      O     R₂    H
     \    |    ‖      ‖      |    /
      N — C — C        C — C — N
     /    |     \     /       |    \
    H     H    ⌐OH   H┐O     H     H
               └ ̄ ̄ ̄ ̄ ̄┘
```

23. Consider the reaction pathway shown.

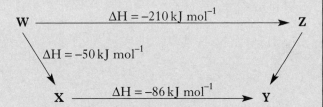

According to Hess' Law, the ΔH value, in kJ mol^{-1}, for reaction **Z** to **Y** is

A +74

B −74

C +346

D −346.

24. Which of the following is likely to apply to the use of a catalyst in a chemical reaction?

	Position of equilibrium	Effect on value of ΔH
A	moved to right	decreased
B	unaffected	increased
C	moved to left	unaffected
D	unaffected	unaffected

25. On the structure shown, four hydrogen atoms have been replaced by letters A, B, C and D.

```
    Ⓐ       H    O—Ⓑ   H          O
     \      |    |      |          ‖
      C — C — C ———— C — C
     ‖      |    |      |           \
     O      H    H      Ⓒ          O—Ⓓ
```

Which letter corresponds to the hydrogen atom which can ionise most easily in aqueous solution?

26. A fully dissociated acid is progressively diluted by the addition of water.

Which of the following would increase with increasing dilution?

A The pH value

B The electrical conductivity

C The rate of its reaction with chalk

D The volume of alkali which it will neutralise

27. Which of the following is a redox reaction?

A $NaOH + HCl \rightarrow NaCl + H_2O$

B $Zn + 2HCl \rightarrow ZnCl_2 + H_2$

C $NiO + 2HCl \rightarrow NiCl_2 + H_2O$

D $CuCO_3 + 2HCl \rightarrow CuCl_2 + H_2O + CO_2$

28. If 96 500 C of electricity are passed through separate solutions of copper(II) chloride and nickel(II) chloride, then

A equal masses of copper and nickel will be deposited

B the same number of atoms of each metal will be deposited

C the metals will be plated on the positive electrode

D different numbers of moles of each metal will be deposited.

29. Strontium-90 is a radioisotope.

What is the neutron to proton ratio in an atom of this isotope?

A 2·37

B 1·00

C 0·730

D 1·37

30. Which equation represents a fusion process?

A $\quad {}^{40}_{19}K \ + \ {}^{0}_{-1}e \ \rightarrow \ {}^{40}_{18}Ar$

B $\quad {}^{2}_{1}H \ + \ {}^{3}_{1}H \ \rightarrow \ {}^{4}_{2}He \ + \ {}^{1}_{0}n$

C $\quad {}^{235}_{92}U \ + \ {}^{1}_{0}n \ \rightarrow \ {}^{90}_{38}Sr \ + \ {}^{144}_{54}Xe \ + \ 2{}^{1}_{0}n$

D $\quad {}^{14}_{7}N \ + \ {}^{1}_{0}n \ \rightarrow \ {}^{14}_{6}C \ + \ {}^{1}_{1}p$

[Turn over

SECTION A

PART 2

In questions 31 to 35 of this part of the paper, an answer is given by circling the appropriate letter (or letters) in the answer grids provided on Part 2 of the answer sheet.

In some questions, two letters are required for full marks.

If more than the correct number of answers is given, marks may be deducted.

In some cases the number of correct responses is NOT identified in the question.

This part of the paper is worth 10 marks.

SAMPLE QUESTION

A	B	C
CH_4	H_2	CO_2
D	E	F
CO	C_2H_6	N_2

(a) Identify the diatomic **compound(s)**.

A	B	C
(D)	E	F

The one correct answer to part (a) is D. This should be circled.

(b) Identify the **two** substances which burn to produce **both** carbon dioxide **and** water.

(A)	B	C
D	(E)	F

As indicated in this question, there are **two** correct answers to part (b). These are A and E.
Both answers are circled.

(c) Identify the substance(s) which can **not** be used as a fuel.

A	B	(C)
D	E	(F)

There are **two** correct answers to part (c). These are C and F.
Both answers are circled.

If, after you have recorded your answer, you decide that you have made an error and wish to make a change, you should cancel the original answer and circle the answer you now consider to be correct. Thus, in part (a), if you want to change an answer **D** to an answer **A**, your answer sheet would look like this:

(A)	B	C
D̸	E	F

If you want to change back to an answer which has already been scored out, you should enter a tick (✓) in the box of the answer of your choice, thus:

A̸	B	C
✓ D̸	E	F

31. The first twenty elements can be arranged according to bonding and structure.

A		B		C	
aluminium		boron		chlorine	
D		**E**		**F**	
hydrogen		phosphorus		silicon	

(a) Identify the element which is a discrete molecular solid at room temperature and pressure.

(b) Identify the **two** elements which combine to form the compound with most covalent character.
(You may wish to use page 10 of the data booklet.)

32. Compounds can have different structures and properties.

A		B		C	
NH_4NO_3		$BaSO_4$		Na_2CO_3	
D		**E**		**F**	
SiO_2		K_2O		P_2O_5	

(a) Identify the compound with a covalent network structure.

(b) Identify the salt which dissolves in water to form an alkaline solution.

[Turn over

33. The symbol for the Avogadro Constant is N_A.

Identify the **true** statement(s).

A	64·2 g of sulphur contains approximately N_A atoms.
B	16·0 g of oxygen contains approximately N_A molecules.
C	6·0 g of water contains approximately N_A atoms.
D	1·0 g of hydrogen contains approximately N_A protons.
E	2·0 litres of 0·50 mol l^{-1} sulphuric acid contains approximately N_A hydrogen ions.
F	1·0 litre of 1·0 mol l^{-1} barium hydroxide solution contains approximately N_A hydroxide ions.

34. Proteins are an important part of a balanced diet.

Identify the **true** statement(s).

A	Proteins are a more concentrated source of energy than carbohydrates.
B	Proteins are made by addition polymerisation.
C	Denaturing of proteins involves changes in the structure of the molecules.
D	Globular proteins are the **major** structural materials of animal tissue.
E	Proteins are compounds of nitrogen, carbon, hydrogen and oxygen.
F	Proteins can be made in animals but **not** in plants.

35. Two flasks contained equal volumes of $0 \cdot 1$ mol l^{-1} hydrochloric acid and $0 \cdot 1$ mol l^{-1} ethanoic acid. Identify the **true** statement(s) about **both** solutions.

A	They give the same colour with Universal indicator.
B	They have a pH less than 7.
C	They conduct electricity equally well.
D	They have equal concentrations of hydrogen ions.
E	They react at the same rate with magnesium.
F	They neutralise the same number of moles of sodium hydroxide.

Candidates are reminded that the answer sheet MUST be returned INSIDE the front cover of this answer book.

[Turn over

Marks

SECTION B

1. The three statements below are taken from a note made by a student who is studying trends in the Periodic Table.

   1   <u>First Ionisation Energy</u>

   The energy required to remove one mole of electrons from one mole of atoms in the gaseous state.

   2   <u>Second Ionisation Energy</u>

   The energy required to remove a second mole of electrons.

   3   _____

   The measure of the attraction an atom has for the shared electrons in a bond.

   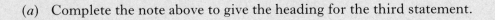

   (a) Complete the note above to give the heading for the third statement.

        1

   (b) What is the trend in the first ionisation energy across a period from left to right?

        1

   (c) Why is the second ionisation energy of sodium so much greater than its first ionisation energy?

        1

        (3)

Marks

2. Carbon dating can be used to estimate the age of charcoal found in archaeological sites.

The graph shows how the count rate of a sample of radioactive carbon-14 changes over a period of time.

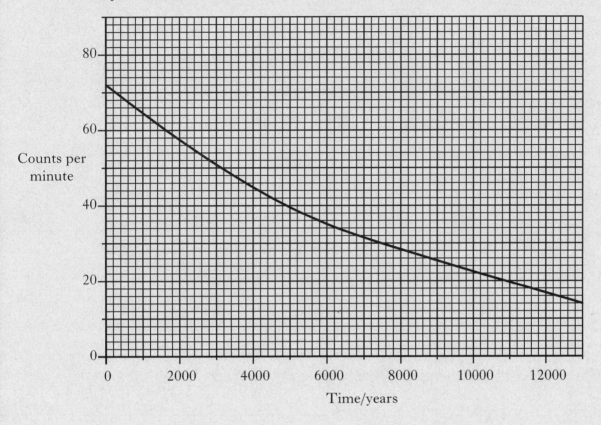

(*a*) Use the graph to find the half-life of carbon-14.

1

(*b*) Carbon-14 decays by beta-emission.

Write the balanced nuclear equation for this decay.

1

(*c*) Why can carbon dating **not** be used to estimate the age of fossil fuels?

1

(3)

Marks

3. The structure of a molecule found in olive oil can be represented as shown.

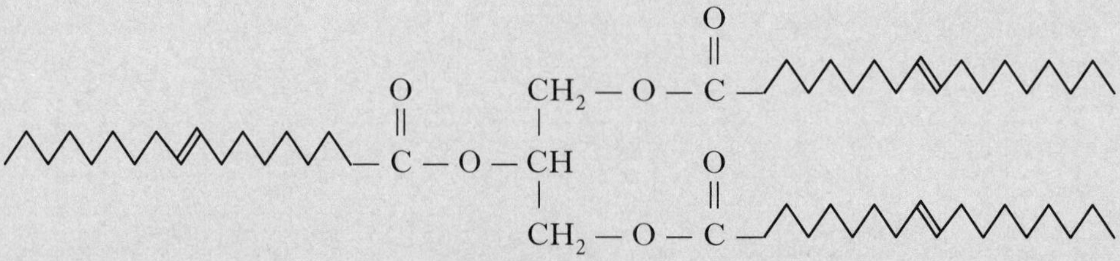

(*a*) Olive oil can be hardened using a nickel catalyst to produce a fat.

   (i) What type of catalyst is nickel in this reaction?

1

   (ii) In what way does the structure of a fat molecule differ from that of an oil molecule?

1

(*b*) Olive oil can be hydrolysed using sodium hydroxide solution to produce sodium salts of fatty acids.

   (i) Name the other product of this reaction.

1

   (ii) Give a commercial use for sodium salts of fatty acids.

1

(4)

Marks

4. Hydrogen sulphide, H_2S, is the unpleasant gas produced when eggs rot.

(a) (i) The gas can be prepared by the reaction of iron(II) sulphide with dilute hydrochloric acid. Iron(II) chloride is the other product of the reaction.

Write a balanced chemical equation for this reaction.

1

(ii) Iron metal is often present as an impurity in iron(II) sulphide.

Name the other product which would be formed in the reaction with dilute hydrochloric acid if iron metal is present as an impurity.

1

(b) The enthalpy of combustion of hydrogen sulphide is $-563\,kJ\,mol^{-1}$.

Use this value and the enthalpy of combustion values in the data booklet to calculate the enthalpy change for the reaction:

$$H_2(g) \quad + \quad \underset{\text{(rhombic)}}{S(s)} \quad \longrightarrow \quad H_2S(g)$$

Show your working clearly.

2

(4)

DO NO
WRITE
THIS
MARGI

Marks

5. An ester can be prepared by the following sequence of reactions.

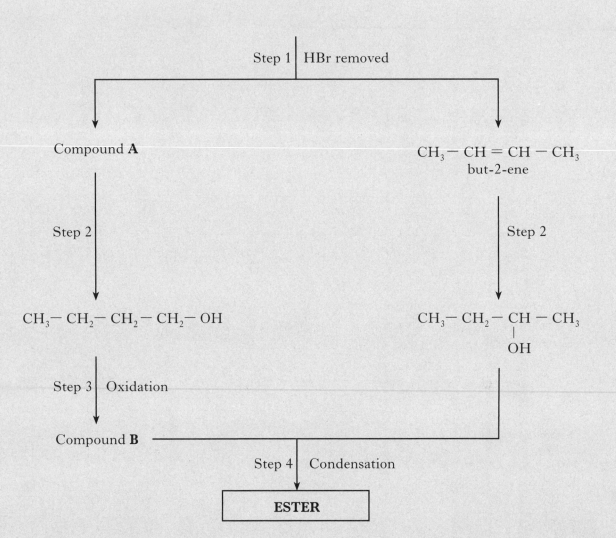

(a) (i) Draw a structural formula for compound **A**.

1

DO NOT WRITE IN THIS MARGIN

Marks

5. (*a*) (continued)

(ii) But-2-ene and compound **A** undergo the same type of reaction in Step 2. Name this type of reaction. **1**

(iii) Acidified potassium dichromate solution can be used to carry out Step 3. What colour change would be observed? **1**

(iv) Name compound **B**. **1**

(*b*) (i) What evidence would show that an ester had been formed in Step 4? **1**

(ii) Give **one** use for esters. **1**

(6)

[Turn over

Marks

6. A calorimeter, like the one shown, can be used to measure the enthalpy of combustion of ethanol.

The ethanol is ignited and burns completely in the oxygen gas. The heat energy released in the reaction is taken in by the water as the hot product gases are drawn through the coiled copper pipe by the pump.

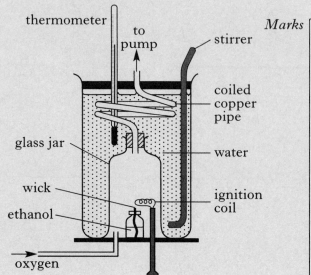

(a) Why is the copper pipe coiled as shown in the diagram?

1

(b) The value for the enthalpy of combustion of ethanol obtained by the calorimeter method is higher than the value obtained by the typical school laboratory method.

One reason for this is that more heat is lost to the surroundings in the typical school laboratory method.

Give **one** other reason for the value being higher with the calorimeter method.

1

(c) In one experiment the burning of $0 \cdot 980$ g of ethanol resulted in the temperature of $400 \, \text{cm}^3$ of water rising from $14 \cdot 2 \, ^\circ\text{C}$ to $31 \cdot 6 \, ^\circ\text{C}$.

Use this information to calculate the enthalpy of combustion of ethanol.

Show your working clearly.

3

DO NOT WRITE IN THIS MARGIN

Marks

7. A mass spectrometer is an instrument that can be used to gain information about the masses of molecules.

When hydrogen fluoride is analysed in a mass spectrometer, as well as molecules with a relative molecular mass of 20, some "double molecules" (relative molecular mass 40) and "triple molecules" (relative molecular mass 60) are found to exist. No such molecules are found when the elements, hydrogen and fluorine, are separately analysed.

(*a*) Name the weak force of attraction between molecules that is found in both liquid hydrogen and liquid fluorine. **1**

(*b*) Why are "double" and "triple" molecules found in hydrogen fluoride but **not** in hydrogen and **not** in fluorine? **1**

(2)

[Turn over

Marks

8. A student added 0.20 g of silver nitrate, $AgNO_3$, to 25 cm^3 of water. This solution was then added to 20 cm^3 of 0.0010 mol l^{-1} hydrochloric acid as shown in the diagram.

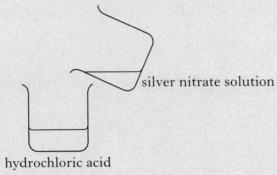

silver nitrate solution

hydrochloric acid

The equation for the reaction which occurs is:

$$AgNO_3(aq) \ + \ HCl(aq) \ \longrightarrow \ AgCl(s) \ + \ HNO_3(aq)$$

(a) (i) Name the type of reaction which takes place.

1

(ii) Show by calculation which reactant is in excess.
Show your working clearly.

2

Marks

8. **(continued)**

(*b*) The hydrochloric acid in the experiment can be described as a dilute solution of a strong acid.

   (i) What is meant by a strong acid?

1

   (ii) What is the pH of the 0.0010 mol l^{-1} hydrochloric acid used in the experiment?

1

(5)

[Turn over

9. The decomposition of hydrogen peroxide solution into water and oxygen can be catalysed by an enzyme.

$$2H_2O_2(aq) \xrightarrow{\text{enzyme}} 2H_2O(\ell) \;+\; O_2(g)$$

The rate of reaction can be followed by recording the mass loss over a period of time.

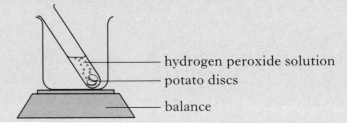

(a) The following graph was obtained from experiments to find the effect of pH on the efficiency of the enzyme.

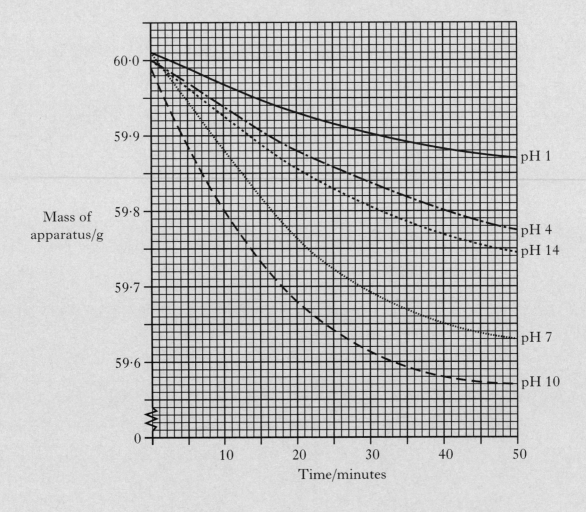

DO NOT
WRITE IN
THIS
MARGIN

Marks

9. (a) (continued)

    (i) Calculate the average rate of reaction over the first 20 minutes, in $g\,min^{-1}$, for the experiment at pH 10.

    2

    (ii) From the results shown on the graph, what can be concluded about the efficiency of the enzyme over the pH range used in the experiment?

    1

    (b) Give **one** other way of following the rate of this reaction.

    1

    (4)

    [Turn over

Marks

10. Consider the following industrial processes.

Contact Process $2SO_2(g) + O_2(g) \rightleftharpoons 2SO_3(g)$ ΔH –ve

Haber Process $N_2(g) + 3H_2(g) \rightleftharpoons 2NH_3(g)$ ΔH –ve

(a) For each process, circle the reactant that can be classified as a raw material. **1**

(b) Explain why increasing the temperature in both processes decreases the equilibrium yield of the products.

2

(c) Suggest why the Contact Process is carried out at atmospheric pressure but the Haber Process is carried out at 400 atmospheres.

1

(d) Under certain conditions, 200 kg of hydrogen reacts with excess nitrogen in the Haber Process to produce 650 kg of ammonia.

Calculate the percentage yield of ammonia.

Show your working clearly.

2

(6)

DO NOT WRITE IN THIS MARGIN

Marks

11. Acrylonitrile, CH_2CHCN, is the monomer used in the manufacture of Acrilan.

(*a*) (i) Draw the full structural formula for acrylonitrile. **1**

(ii) Name the type of polymerisation which occurs in the manufacture of Acrilan. **1**

(*b*) Acrylonitrile can be reduced in neutral aqueous solution forming $(CH_2CH_2CN)_2$. Hydroxide ions are also produced in the reaction.

Complete and balance the ion-electron equation for the reduction reaction described above.

$$CH_2CHCN \longrightarrow (CH_2CH_2CN)_2 + OH^-$$

1

(3)

[Turn over

Marks

12. When sodium hydrogencarbonate is heated to 112 °C it decomposes and the gas, carbon dioxide, is given off:

$$2NaHCO_3(s) \longrightarrow Na_2CO_3(s) + CO_2(g) + H_2O(g)$$

The following apparatus can be used to measure the volume of carbon dioxide produced by the reaction.

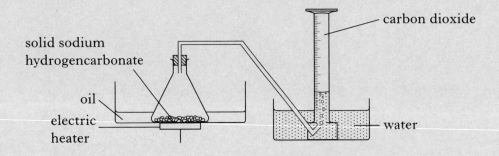

(*a*) Why is an oil bath used and **not** a water bath?

1

(*b*) (i) Calculate the theoretical volume of carbon dioxide produced by the complete decomposition of 1·68 g of sodium hydrogencarbonate.

(Take the molar volume of carbon dioxide to be 23 litre mol^{-1}.)

Show your working clearly.

2

(ii) Assuming that all of the sodium hydrogencarbonate is decomposed, suggest why the volume of carbon dioxide collected in the measuring cylinder would be less than the theoretical value.

1

(4)

Marks

13. Alkenes can react with oxygen to produce unstable compounds called peroxides. These peroxides break down rapidly to form compounds which have the same functional group.

For example, alkene **X** reacts to produce compounds **Y** and **Z**.

(In the following structural formulae R' and R" are used to represent different alkyl groups.)

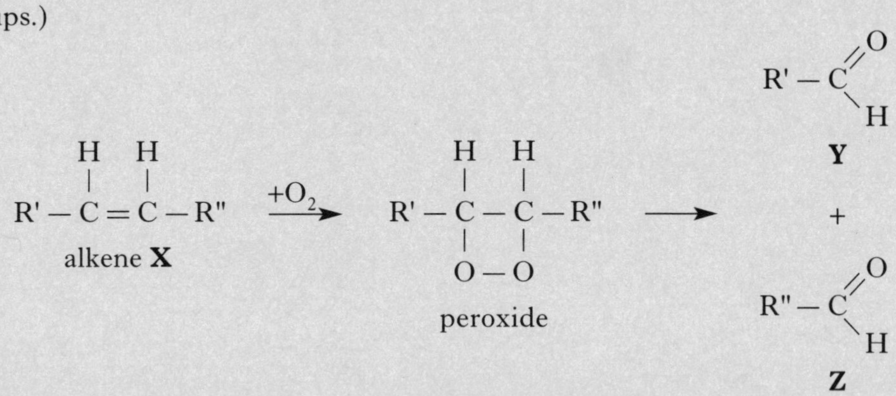

$$R' - \overset{\overset{\displaystyle H}{|}}{C} = \overset{\overset{\displaystyle H}{|}}{C} - R'' \xrightarrow{+O_2} R' - \overset{\overset{\displaystyle H}{|}}{\underset{\underset{\displaystyle O}{|}}{C}} - \overset{\overset{\displaystyle H}{|}}{\underset{\underset{\displaystyle O}{|}}{C}} - R'' \longrightarrow$$

alkene **X**   peroxide

$$R' - C \overset{\displaystyle O}{\underset{\displaystyle H}{<}}$$

Y

+

$$R'' - C \overset{\displaystyle O}{\underset{\displaystyle H}{<}}$$

Z

(a) To which homologous series do both compounds **Y** and **Z** belong?

1

(b) In one reaction, alkene **X** reacts to produce the two compounds shown below.

$$CH_3 - C \overset{\displaystyle O}{\underset{\displaystyle H}{<}}$$

Y

$$CH_3 - \overset{\overset{\displaystyle CH_3}{|}}{\underset{\underset{\displaystyle H}{|}}{C}} - C \overset{\displaystyle O}{\underset{\displaystyle H}{<}}$$

Z

Name alkene **X** in this reaction.

1

(2)

[Turn over

Marks

14. The concentration of a solution of sodium thiosulphate can be found by reaction with iodine.

The iodine is produced by electrolysis of an iodide solution using the apparatus shown.

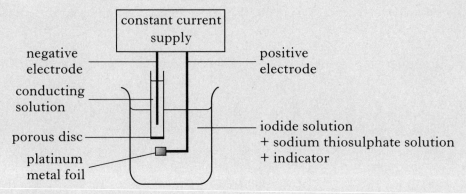

The current is noted and the time when the indicator detects the end-point of the reaction is recorded.

(a) Iodine is produced from the iodide solution according to the following equation:

$$2I^-(aq) \longrightarrow I_2(aq) + 2e^-$$

Calculate the number of moles of iodine generated during the electrolysis given the following results.

Current = 0·010 A
Time   = 1 min 37 s

Show your working clearly.

2

Marks

14. **(continued)**

(*b*) The iodine produced reacts with the thiosulphate ions according to the equation:

$$I_2(aq) \quad + \quad 2S_2O_3^{2-}(aq) \quad \longrightarrow \quad 2I^-(aq) \quad + \quad S_4O_6^{2-}(aq)$$

  iodine   thiosulphate ions

At the end-point of the reaction, excess iodine is detected by the indicator.

(i) Name the indicator which could be used to detect the excess iodine present at the end-point.

1

(ii) In a second experiment it was found that $1 \cdot 2 \times 10^{-5}$ mol of iodine reacted with $3 \cdot 0 \, cm^3$ of the sodium thiosulphate solution.

Use this information to calculate the concentration of the sodium thiosulphate solution, in $mol \, l^{-1}$.

Show your working clearly.

2

(iii) The production of iodine takes place at the surface of the platinum foil at the tip of the positive electrode.

Suggest what could be done to the solution during the reaction to increase the accuracy of the results.

1

(6)

[Turn over

DO NOT
WRITE IN
THIS
MARGIN

Marks

15. Although they are more expensive, fuel cells have been developed as an alternative to petrol for motor vehicles.

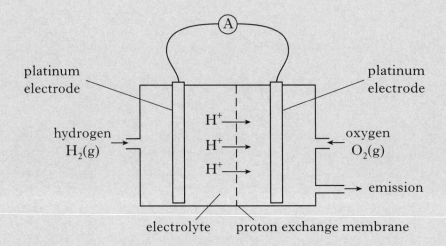

(*a*) (i) The ion-electron equations for the process occurring at each electrode are:

$$H_2(g) \longrightarrow 2H^+(aq) + 2e^-$$

$$O_2(g) + 4H^+(aq) + 4e^- \longrightarrow 2H_2O(\ell)$$

Combine these two equations to give the overall redox equation.

1

(ii) On the diagram, show by means of an arrow, the path of electron flow.

1

(*b*) Give **one** advantage that fuel cells have over petrol for providing energy.

1

(3)

[END OF QUESTION PAPER]

2003 HIGHER

FOR OFFICIAL USE

Total
Section B

X012/301

NATIONAL
QUALIFICATIONS
2003

FRIDAY, 23 MAY
1.00 PM – 3.30 PM

CHEMISTRY
HIGHER

Fill in these boxes and read what is printed below.

Full name of centre

Town

Forename(s)

Surname

Date of birth
Day Month Year   Scottish candidate number   Number of seat

Reference may be made to the Chemistry Higher and Advanced Higher Data Booklet (1999 edition).

SECTION A—Questions 1–40

Instructions for completion of **Section A** are given on page two.

SECTION B

1   All questions should be attempted.

2   The questions may be answered in any order but all answers are to be written in the spaces provided in this answer book, and must be written clearly and legibly in ink.

3   Rough work, if any should be necessary, should be written in this book and then scored through when the fair copy has been written.

4   Additional space for answers and rough work will be found at the end of the book. If further space is required, supplementary sheets may be obtained from the invigilator and should be inserted inside the **front** cover of this book.

5   The size of the space provided for an answer should not be taken as an indication of how much to write. It is not necessary to use all the space.

6   Before leaving the examination room you must give this book to the invigilator. If you do not, you may lose all the marks for this paper.

SCOTTISH
QUALIFICATIONS
AUTHORITY

©

SECTION A

1. Check that the answer sheet provided is for Chemistry Higher (Section A).

2. Fill in the details required on the answer sheet.

3. **In questions 1 to 40 of the paper, an answer is given by indicating the choice A, B, C or D by a stroke made in INK in the appropriate place in the answer sheet—see the sample question below.**

4. **For each question there is only ONE correct answer.**

5. Rough working, if required, should be done only on this question paper, or on the rough working sheet provided—**not** on the answer sheet.

6. At the end of the examination the answer sheet for Section A **must** be placed **inside** the front cover of this answer book.

This part of the paper is worth 40 marks.

SAMPLE QUESTION

To show that the ink in a ball-pen consists of a mixture of dyes, the method of separation would be

        A   fractional distillation

        B   chromatography

        C   fractional crystallisation

        D   filtration.

The correct answer is B—chromatography. A **heavy** vertical line should be drawn joining the two dots in the appropriate box in the column headed **B** as shown **in the example on the answer sheet**.

If, after you have recorded your answer, you decide that you have made an error and wish to make a change, you should cancel the original answer and put a vertical stroke in the box you now consider to be correct. Thus, if you want to change an answer **D** to an answer **B**, your answer sheet would look like this:

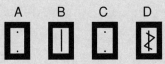

If you want to change back to an answer which has already been scored out, you should **enter a tick (✓)** to the RIGHT of the box of your choice, thus:

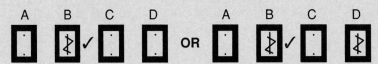

1. Which of the following substances is a non-conductor when solid, but becomes a good conductor on melting?

   A Argon

   B Potassium

   C Potassium fluoride

   D Tetrachloromethane

2. Which of the following covalent gases does **not** react with water forming ions?

   A HCl

   B SO_2

   C NH_3

   D CH_4

3. An iron nail is covered with water.

   Which of the following procedures would **not** increase the rate at which the iron nail corrodes?

   A Adding some sodium sulphate to the water

   B Adding some glucose to the water

   C Attaching a copper wire to the nail

   D Passing carbon dioxide through the water

4. Naturally occurring nitrogen consists of two isotopes ^{14}N and ^{15}N.

   How many different types of nitrogen molecules will occur in the air?

   A 1

   B 2

   C 3

   D 4

5. A mixture of sodium chloride and sodium sulphate is known to contain 0·6 mol of chloride ions and 0·2 mol of sulphate ions.

   How many moles of sodium ions are present?

   A 0·4

   B 0·5

   C 0·8

   D 1·0

6. When copper carbonate reacts with excess acid, carbon dioxide is produced. The curves shown were obtained under different conditions.

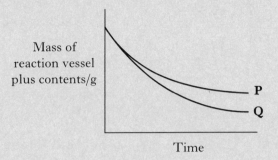

   The change from **P** to **Q** could be brought about by

   A increasing the concentration of the acid

   B increasing the mass of copper carbonate

   C decreasing the particle size of the copper carbonate

   D adding a catalyst.

7. When 3·6 g of butanal (relative formula mass = 72) was burned, 134 kJ of energy was released.

   From this result, what is the enthalpy of combustion, in $kJ\,mol^{-1}$?

   A −6·7

   B +6·7

   C −2680

   D +2680

8. Which of the following chlorides is likely to have the **most** ionic character?

   A LiCl

   B CsCl

   C $BeCl_2$

   D $CaCl_2$

9. Which equation represents the first ionisation energy of a diatomic element, X_2?

   A $\frac{1}{2}X_2(s) \rightarrow X^+(g)$

   B $\frac{1}{2}X_2(g) \rightarrow X^-(g)$

   C $X(g) \rightarrow X^+(g)$

   D $X(s) \rightarrow X^-(g)$

[Turn over

10. Which of the following elements exists as discrete molecules?

   A   Boron

   B   Carbon (diamond)

   C   Silicon

   D   Sulphur

11. Which of the following chlorides is most likely to be soluble in tetrachloromethane, CCl_4?

   A   Barium chloride

   B   Caesium chloride

   C   Calcium chloride

   D   Phosphorus chloride

12. In which of the following liquids does hydrogen bonding occur?

   A   Ethanoic acid

   B   Ethyl ethanoate

   C   Hexane

   D   Hex-1-ene

13. A compound boils at −33 °C. It also dissolves in water to give an alkaline solution.

   Which type of bonding is present within the compound?

   A   Metallic

   B   Covalent (polar)

   C   Ionic

   D   Covalent (non-polar)

14. The number of moles of ions in 1 mol of copper(II) phosphate is

   A   1

   B   2

   C   4

   D   5.

15. The Avogadro Constant is the same as the number of

   A   atoms in 24 g of carbon

   B   molecules in 16 g of oxygen

   C   molecules in 2 g of hydrogen

   D   ions in 1 litre of sodium chloride solution, concentration $1 \, mol \, l^{-1}$.

16. What volume of oxygen, in litres, is required for the complete combustion of 1 litre of butane gas?

   (All volumes are measured under the same conditions of temperature and pressure.)

   A   1

   B   4

   C   6·5

   D   13

17. Which of the following processes can be used industrially to produce aromatic hydrocarbons?

   A   Reforming of naphtha

   B   Catalytic cracking of propane

   C   Reforming of coal

   D   Catalytic cracking of heavy oil fractions

18. Which line in the table refers to a hydrocarbon that is **not** a member of the same homologous series as the others?

	Relative formula mass
A	44
B	72
C	84
D	100

19. Which of the following compounds does **not** have isomeric structures?

   A C_2HCl_3

   B $C_2H_4Cl_2$

   C   Propene

   D   Propan-1-ol

20. Which of the following structural formulae represents a tertiary alcohol?

$$A \quad CH_3 - \underset{\underset{CH_3}{|}}{\overset{\overset{CH_3}{|}}{C}} - CH_2 - OH$$

$$B \quad CH_3 - \underset{\underset{OH}{|}}{\overset{\overset{CH_3}{|}}{C}} - CH_2 - CH_3$$

$$C \quad CH_3 - CH_2 - CH_2 - \underset{\underset{OH}{|}}{\overset{\overset{H}{|}}{C}} - CH_3$$

$$D \quad CH_3 - CH_2 - \underset{\underset{OH}{|}}{\overset{\overset{H}{|}}{C}} - CH_2 - CH_3$$

21. Oxidation of 4-methylpentan-2-ol to the corresponding ketone results in the alcohol

A losing 2 g per mole

B gaining 2 g per mole

C gaining 16 g per mole

D not changing in mass.

22. What type of reaction takes place when propene is formed from propanol?

A Condensation

B Hydrolysis

C Dehydration

D Hydration

23. The extensive use of which type of compound is thought to contribute significantly to the depletion of the ozone layer?

A Oxides of carbon

B Hydrocarbons

C Oxides of sulphur

D Chlorofluorocarbons

24. Polyesters can exist as fibres and cured resins.

Which line in the table describes correctly the structure of their molecules?

	Polyester fibre	Cured polyester resin
A	cross-linked	cross-linked
B	linear	linear
C	cross-linked	linear
D	linear	cross-linked

25. Ammonia solution may be used to distinguish $Fe^{2+}(aq)$ from $Fe^{3+}(aq)$ as follows:

$Fe^{2+}(aq)$ gives a green precipitate of $Fe(OH)_2$;

$Fe^{3+}(aq)$ gives a brown precipitate of $Fe(OH)_3$.

Which of the following is most likely to give similar results if used instead of ammonia?

A An amine

B An alcohol

C An aldehyde

D A carboxylic acid

26. In the formation of "hardened" fats from vegetable oils, the hydrogen

A causes cross-linking between chains

B causes hydrolysis to occur

C increases the carbon chain length

D reduces the number of carbon-carbon double bonds.

[Turn over

27. Olestra is a calorie free fat made by reacting fatty acids with sucrose. The structure of a sucrose molecule can be represented as shown.

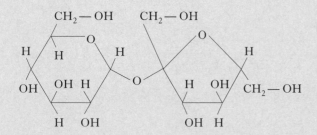

How many fatty acid molecules can react with one molecule of sucrose?

A   3

B   5

C   8

D   11

28. Proteins can be denatured under acid conditions.

During this denaturing, the protein molecule

A   changes shape

B   is dehydrated

C   is neutralised

D   is polymerised.

29. Which of the following substances is a raw material for the chemical industry?

A   Benzene

B   Methane

C   Aluminium

D   Iron

30. What is the relationship between enthalpies p, q, r and s?

$$S(s) \ + \ H_2(g) \ \rightarrow \ H_2S(g)$$
$$\Delta H = p$$
$$H_2(g) \ + \ \tfrac{1}{2}O_2(g) \ \rightarrow \ H_2O(\ell)$$
$$\Delta H = q$$
$$S(s) \ + \ O_2(g) \ \rightarrow \ SO_2(g)$$
$$\Delta H = r$$
$$H_2S(g) + 1\tfrac{1}{2}O_2(g) \ \rightarrow \ H_2O(\ell)+SO_2(g)$$
$$\Delta H = s$$

A $p = q + r - s$

B $p = s - q - r$

C $p = q - r - s$

D $p = s + r - q$

31. A catalyst is added to a reaction at equilibrium.

Which of the following does **not** apply?

A   The rate of the forward reaction increases.

B   The rate of the reverse reaction increases.

C   The position of equilibrium remains unchanged.

D   The position of equilibrium shifts to the right.

32. $ICl(\ell) \ + \ Cl_2(g) \ \rightleftharpoons \ ICl_3(s) \quad \Delta H = -106 \, kJ \, mol^-$

Which line in the table identifies correctly the changes that will cause the greatest increase in the proportion of solid in the above equilibrium?

	Temperature	Pressure
A	decrease	decrease
B	decrease	increase
C	increase	decrease
D	increase	increase

33. Which of the following is the best description of a $0\cdot1 \, mol \, l^{-1}$ solution of ethanoic acid?

A   Dilute solution of a weak acid

B   Dilute solution of a strong acid

C   Concentrated solution of a weak acid

D   Concentrated solution of a strong acid

34. The concentration of $OH^-(aq)$ ions in a solution is 1×10^{-2} mol l^{-1}.

What is the concentration of $H^+(aq)$ ions, in mol l^{-1}?

A 1×10^{-2}

B 1×10^{-5}

C 1×10^{-9}

D 1×10^{-12}

35. When a certain aqueous solution is diluted, its conductivity decreases but its pH remains constant.

The solution could be

A ethanoic acid

B sodium chloride

C sodium hydroxide

D nitric acid.

36. The ion-electron equations for a redox reaction are:

$2I^-(aq) \rightarrow I_2(aq) + 2e^-$
$MnO_4^-(aq) + 8H^+(aq) + 5e^- \rightarrow Mn^{2+}(aq) + 4H_2O(\ell)$

How many moles of iodide ions are oxidised by one mole of permanganate ions?

A 0·2

B 0·4

C 2

D 5

37. In which of the following reactions is hydrogen gas acting as an oxidising agent?

A $H_2 + C_2H_4 \rightarrow C_2H_6$

B $H_2 + Cl_2 \rightarrow 2HCl$

C $H_2 + 2Na \rightarrow 2NaH$

D $H_2 + CuO \rightarrow H_2O + Cu$

38. When 10 g of lead pellets containing radioactive lead are placed in a solution containing 10 g of lead nitrate, radioactivity soon appears in the solution.

Compared to the pellets the solution will show

A different intensity of radiation and different half-life

B the same intensity of radiation but different half-life

C different intensity of radiation but the same half-life

D the same intensity of radiation and the same half-life.

39. Which line in the table describes correctly the result of an atom losing a beta-particle?

	Atomic number	Mass number
A	increased	no change
B	decreased	no change
C	no change	increased
D	no change	decreased

40. $^2_1H + ^3_1H \rightarrow ^4_2He + ^1_0n$

The above process represents

A nuclear fission

B nuclear fusion

C proton capture

D neutron capture.

[Turn over

DO NO
WRITE
THIS
MARGI

SECTION B

Marks

1. Unleaded petrol uses hydrocarbons with a high degree of molecular branching in order to improve the efficiency of burning.

   The structure of one such hydrocarbon is shown.

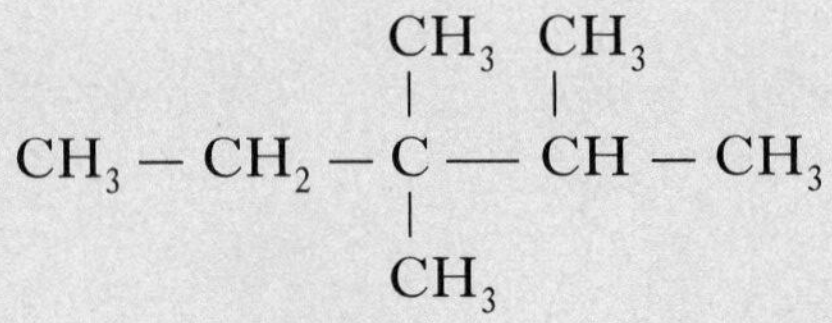

$$CH_3 - CH_2 - \overset{\overset{\displaystyle CH_3}{|}}{\underset{\underset{\displaystyle CH_3}{|}}{C}} - \overset{\overset{\displaystyle CH_3}{|}}{CH} - CH_3$$

   (a) Give the systematic name for this hydrocarbon.

1

   (b) Name **one** other **type** of hydrocarbon that is used in petrol for the same reason.

1

(2)

Marks

2. Concorde aircraft were grounded after an incident in which the fuel tank in one of the aeroplanes was punctured by a piece of metal. As a result the fuel tanks are now coated with the polymer, Kevlar.

(*a*) What property of Kevlar makes it suitable for this use?

1

(*b*) The repeating unit in Kevlar is shown.

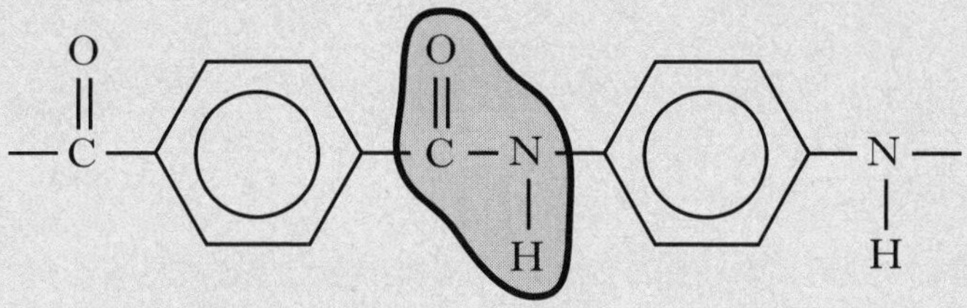

What name is given to the outlined group in this repeating unit?

1
(2)

[Turn over

Marks

3. Polonium-210 is a radioisotope that decays by alpha-emission.

The half-life of polonium-210 is 140 days.

(*a*) Draw a graph to show how the mass of 200 g of the radioisotope would change with time.

(Additional graph paper, if required, can be found on page 32.)

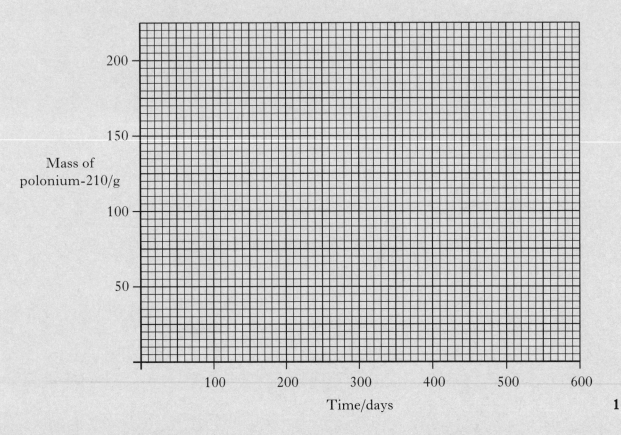

1

(*b*) Write a balanced nuclear equation for the alpha-decay of polonium-210.

1

(*c*) Calculate the number of atoms in 105 g of polonium-210.

1

(3)

Marks

4. The Thermite Process involves the reaction between aluminium and iron(III) oxide to produce iron and aluminium oxide.

This highly exothermic reaction, which generates so much heat that the temperature of the mixture rises to around 3000 °C, is used for repairing cracked railway lines as shown in the diagram below.

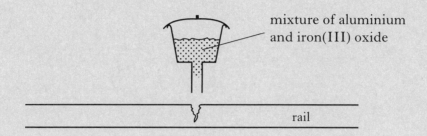

mixture of aluminium and iron(III) oxide

rail

(*a*) Suggest why this process is suitable for repairing cracked railway lines.

1

(*b*) The enthalpy changes for the formation of one mole of aluminium oxide and one mole of iron(III) oxide are shown below.

$$2Al(s) \ + \ 1\tfrac{1}{2}O_2(g) \longrightarrow Al_2O_3(s) \quad \Delta H = -1676 \, kJ \, mol^{-1}$$
$$2Fe(s) \ + \ 1\tfrac{1}{2}O_2(g) \longrightarrow Fe_2O_3(s) \quad \Delta H = -825 \, kJ \, mol^{-1}$$

Use the above information to calculate the enthalpy change for the reaction:

$$2Al(s) \ + \ Fe_2O_3(s) \longrightarrow Al_2O_3(s) \ + \ 2Fe(s)$$

1

(2)

[Turn over

Marks

5. Urea-methanal is a polymer which can be made using coal as a feedstock.

The flow diagram shows the steps involved in the production of the polymer.

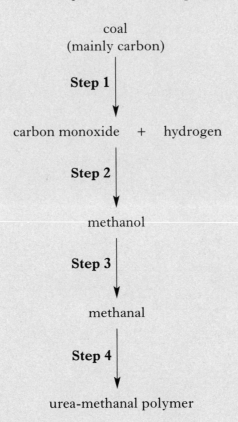

coal
(mainly carbon)

Step 1

carbon monoxide + hydrogen

Step 2

methanol

Step 3

methanal

Step 4

urea-methanal polymer

(*a*) Name the mixture of gases produced in **Step 1**.

1

(*b*) Name the type of reaction taking place in **Step 3**.

1

DO NOT WRITE IN THIS MARGIN

Marks

5. (continued)

(*c*) (i) In **Step 4** methanal reacts with urea, H_2NCONH_2.
Draw the full structural formula for urea. **1**

(ii) The urea-methanal polymer does **not** soften on heating.
What name is given to this type of plastic? **1**

(4)

[Turn over

DO NOT
WRITE I
THIS
MARGIN

Marks

6. Ethyl pentanoate is an ester. It can be prepared in the lab as shown below.

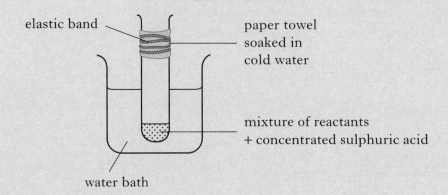

elastic band — paper towel soaked in cold water

mixture of reactants + concentrated sulphuric acid

water bath

(*a*) (i) Why is a water bath used for heating?

1

(ii) What is the purpose of the wet paper towel?

1

(*b*) Draw a structural formula for ethyl pentanoate.

1

Marks

6.   **(continued)**

(*c*)   Starting with a mass of 3·6 g of ethanol, and a slight excess of pentanoic acid, a student achieved a 70% yield of ethyl pentanoate (mass of one mole = 130 g).

Calculate the mass of ester obtained.

Show your working clearly.

2

(5)

[Turn over

Marks

7. A student added $50 \, cm^3$ of $4 \cdot 0 \, mol \, l^{-1}$ hydrochloric acid to $4 \cdot 0 \, g$ of magnesium ribbon.

(*a*) The balanced equation for the reaction is:

$$Mg(s) \quad + \quad 2HCl(aq) \quad \longrightarrow \quad MgCl_2(aq) \quad + \quad H_2(g)$$

Show by calculation which reactant was in excess.

Show your working clearly.

2

(*b*) The hydrogen produced in the reaction can be contaminated with small quantities of hydrogen chloride vapour.

This vapour is very soluble in water.

Complete the diagram to show how the hydrogen chloride can be removed before the hydrogen is collected.

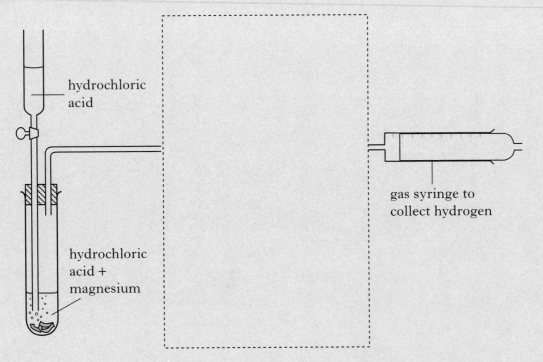

1

DO NOT WRITE IN THIS MARGIN

Marks

7. (continued)

(*c*) The experiment was repeated under the same conditions using ethanoic acid instead of hydrochloric acid.

Circle the correct words in the table to show the results for ethanoic acid.

	Ethanoic acid
Rate of reaction	faster/same/slower
Volume of gas produced	more/same/less

1

(4)

[Turn over

Marks

8. Although aldehydes and ketones have different structures, they both contain the carbonyl functional group.

(*a*) (i) In what way is the structure of an aldehyde different from that of a ketone?

1

(ii) As a result of the difference in structure, aldehydes react with Fehling's (or Benedict's) solution and Tollens' reagent but ketones do not.

What colour change would be observed when propanal is heated with Fehling's (or Benedict's) solution?

1

(iii) In the reaction of propanal with Tollens' reagent, silver ions are reduced to form silver metal.

Complete the following ion-electron equation for the oxidation.

$$C_3H_6O \longrightarrow C_2H_5COOH$$

1

(iv) Name the compound with the formula C_2H_5COOH.

1

Marks

8.   (continued)

(*b*)   As a result of both containing the carbonyl group, aldehydes and ketones react in a similar way with hydrogen cyanide.

The equation for the reaction of propanal and hydrogen cyanide is shown.

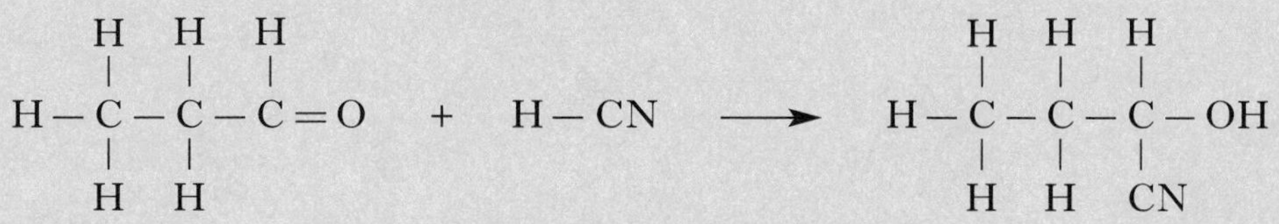

$$
\begin{array}{c}
\quad\ \ \text{H}\ \ \ \text{H}\ \ \ \text{H} \\
\quad\ \ |\ \ \ \ \ |\ \ \ \ \ | \\
\text{H}-\text{C}-\text{C}-\text{C}=\text{O} \qquad + \qquad \text{H}-\text{CN} \qquad\longrightarrow \\
\quad\ \ |\ \ \ \ \ | \\
\quad\ \ \text{H}\ \ \ \text{H}
\end{array}
\qquad
\begin{array}{c}
\ \ \ \text{H}\ \ \ \text{H}\ \ \ \text{H} \\
\ \ \ |\ \ \ \ \ |\ \ \ \ \ | \\
\text{H}-\text{C}-\text{C}-\text{C}-\text{OH} \\
\ \ \ |\ \ \ \ \ |\ \ \ \ \ | \\
\ \ \ \text{H}\ \ \ \text{H}\ \ \ \text{CN}
\end{array}
$$

(i)   Suggest a name for this type of reaction.

1

(ii)   Draw a structure for the product of the reaction between propanone and hydrogen cyanide.

1

(6)

[Turn over

Marks

9. A student was asked to write a plan of the procedure for an investigation. The entry made in her laboratory note book is shown.

Aim

To find the effect of concentration on the rate of the reaction between hydrogen peroxide and an acidified solution of iodide ions.

$$H_2O_2(aq) + 2H^+(aq) + 2I^-(aq) \rightarrow 2H_2O(\ell) + I_2(aq)$$

Procedure

1. Using a $100\,cm^3$ measuring cylinder, measure out $10\,cm^3$ of sulphuric acid, $10\,cm^3$ of sodium thiosulphate solution, $1\,cm^3$ of starch solution and $25\,cm^3$ of potassium iodide solution into a dry $100\,cm^3$ glass beaker and place the beaker on the bench.

2. Measure out $5\,cm^3$ of hydrogen peroxide solution and start the timer.

3. Add the hydrogen peroxide solution to the beaker. When the blue/black colour just appears, stop the timer and record the time (in seconds).

4. Repeat this procedure four times but using different concentrations of potassium iodide solution. This is achieved by adding $5\,cm^3$, $10\,cm^3$, $15\,cm^3$ and $20\,cm^3$ of water to the $25\,cm^3$ of potassium iodide solution before adding it to the glass beaker.

(a) Why is instruction 4 **not** the best way of altering the concentration of the potassium iodide solution?

1

(b) State **two** other ways of improving the student's plan of this investigation procedure.

1

(2)

Marks

10. If both potassium iodide solution, KI(aq), and liquid chloroform, $CHCl_3(\ell)$, are added to a test-tube with some iodine, the iodine dissolves in both. Two layers are formed as shown in the diagram.

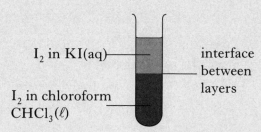

I_2 in KI(aq) — interface between layers

I_2 in chloroform $CHCl_3(\ell)$

An equilibrium is set up:

$$I_2 \text{ in KI(aq)} \rightleftharpoons I_2 \text{ in } CHCl_3(\ell)$$

The iodine is always distributed between the two layers in the same ratio:

$$\frac{\text{concentration of } I_2 \text{ in } CHCl_3(\ell)}{\text{concentration of } I_2 \text{ in KI(aq)}} = \frac{3}{1}$$

(*a*) What is meant by the term **equilibrium**?

1

(*b*) When more potassium iodide solution is added to the top layer the equilibrium is disturbed.

What happens to restore the equilibrium?

1

(*c*) $0.4\,g$ of I_2 is dissolved in $10\,cm^3$ of KI(aq) and $10\,cm^3$ of $CHCl_3(\ell)$.

Calculate the concentration of iodine, **in g l⁻¹**, contained in $CHCl_3(\ell)$.

1

(3)

Marks

11. Hydrogen peroxide, H_2O_2, decomposes very slowly to produce water and oxygen.

(a) The activation energy (E_A) for the reaction is **75 kJ mol^{-1}** and the enthalpy change (ΔH) is **–26 kJ mol^{-1}**.

Use this information to complete the potential energy diagram for the reaction.

(Additional graph paper, if required, can be found on page 32.)

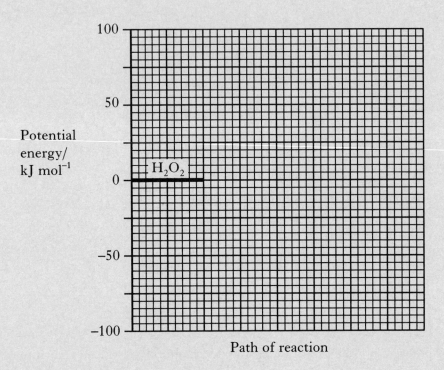

Path of reaction

1

(b) Powdered manganese dioxide catalyses the decomposition of hydrogen peroxide solution.

   (i) What name is given to this type of catalyst?

1

   (ii) Add a dotted line to the above diagram to show the path of the reaction when the catalyst is used.

1

Marks

11. **(continued)**

(c) The balanced equation for the reaction is:

$$2H_2O_2(aq) \longrightarrow 2H_2O(\ell) + O_2(g)$$

(i) The following graph is obtained for the volume of oxygen released over time.

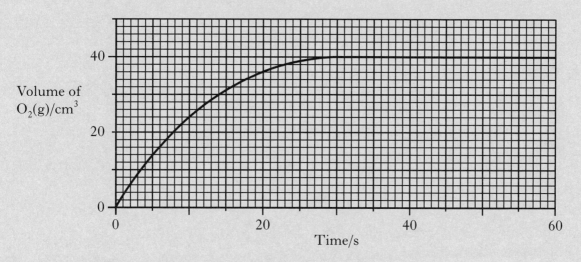

Calculate the average rate of reaction between 10 and 20 s.

1

(ii) Using information from the above graph, calculate the mass of hydrogen peroxide used in the reaction, assuming all the hydrogen peroxide decomposed.

(Take the molar volume of oxygen to be 24 litres mol^{-1}.)

Show your working clearly.

2

(6)

Marks

12. Although propane and ethanol have similar molecular masses, the alkane is a gas at room temperature while the alcohol is a liquid. This difference in boiling points is due to the different strengths of the intermolecular forces in the two compounds.

    Explain why propane is a gas at room temperature while ethanol is a liquid.

    In your answer you should name the intermolecular forces involved in each compound and explain how they arise.

(4)

Marks

13. Potassium cyanide, KCN, can be made by the reaction of an acid with an alkali.
A solution of the salt has a pH of 8.

(*a*) What is the concentration of $H^+(aq)$, in $mol\,l^{-1}$, in the solution?

1

(*b*) What can be concluded about the strengths of the acid and the alkali used in the reaction?

1

(*c*) Write the formula for the acid used in the reaction.

1
(3)

[Turn over

Marks

14. The following flow diagram outlines the manufacture of sodium carbonate by the Solvay Process.

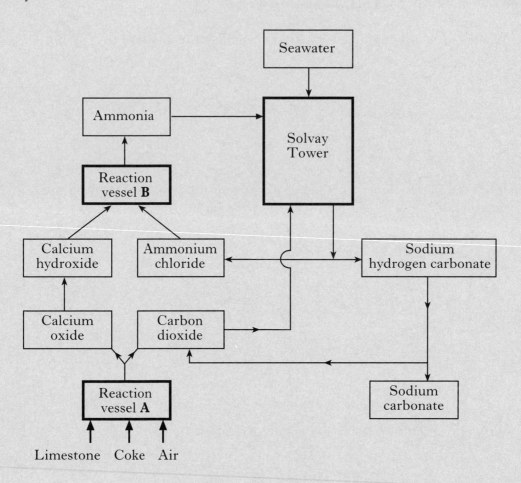

(a) Name the reactants in the reaction taking place in the Solvay Tower.

1

(b) In reaction vessel **A**, carbon dioxide is produced by the following two reactions.

$$CaCO_3(s) \rightarrow CaO(s) + CO_2(g) \qquad \Delta H = \text{_____}$$

$$C(s) + O_2(g) \rightarrow CO_2(g) \qquad \Delta H = \text{_____}$$

For each reaction, add a sign after the ΔH to show whether the reaction is endothermic or exothermic.

1

Marks

14. (continued)

(c) As well as ammonia, a salt and water are produced in reaction vessel **B**.

Write a balanced equation for the production of ammonia in this reaction vessel.

1

(d) The seawater used in the Solvay Process can contain contaminant magnesium ions. These can be removed by the addition of sodium carbonate solution.

Why is sodium carbonate solution suitable for removing contaminant magnesium ions?

1

(e) Using the information in the flow diagram, give **two different** features of the Solvay Process that make it economical.

2

(6)

[Turn over

Marks

15. Electrophoresis, widely used in medicine and forensic testing, involves the movement of ions in an electric field. The technique can be used to separate and identify amino acids produced by the breakdown of proteins.

(a) Name the type of reaction that takes place during the breakdown of proteins.

1

(b) (i) The amino acid, glycine, has the following structural formula:

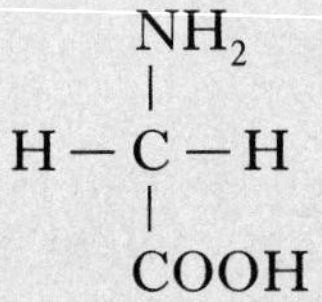

$$
\begin{array}{c}
NH_2 \\
| \\
H-C-H \\
| \\
COOH
\end{array}
$$

Like all amino acids, glycine exists as ions in solution and the charge on the ions depends on the pH of the solution. In solutions with **low** pH, glycine exists as a **positively** charged ion:

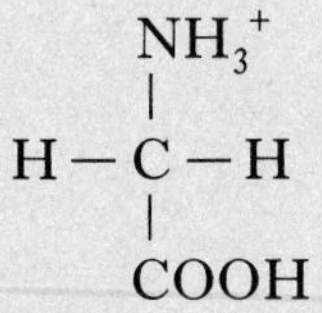

$$
\begin{array}{c}
NH_3^+ \\
| \\
H-C-H \\
| \\
COOH
\end{array}
$$

In solutions with a **high** pH, glycine exists as a **negatively** charged ion.

Draw the structure of this negatively charged ion.

1

DO NOT
WRITE IN
THIS
MARGIN

Marks

15. (*b*) **(continued)**

(ii) The table below shows the structures and molecular masses of three amino acids, **A**, **B** and **C**.

Amino acid	Structure	Molecular mass
A	NH$_2$ | H — C — CH$_2$ —⬡ | COOH	165·0
B	NH$_2$ | H — C — CH$_2$CH$_2$CH$_2$CH$_2$ — **NH$_2$** | COOH	146·0
C	NH$_2$ | H — C — CH$_2$CH$_2$ — **COOH** | COOH	147·0

A mixture of amino acids, **A**, **B** and **C**, was applied to the centre of a strip of filter paper which had been soaked in a solution of pH 2. All three amino acids exist as ions in this acidic solution. A high voltage was then applied across the filter paper.

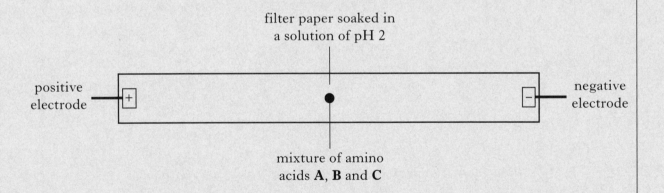

filter paper soaked in
a solution of pH 2

positive
electrode

+

−

negative
electrode

mixture of amino
acids **A**, **B** and **C**

The amino acid ions separate according to their **charge** and **molecular mass**.

On the diagram above, indicate the approximate positions of **A**, **B** and **C** once electrophoresis has separated the ions.

2

(4)

[Turn over

DO NO
WRITE
THIS
MARGI

Marks

16. A student electrolysed dilute sulphuric acid using the apparatus shown in order to estimate the volume of one mole of hydrogen gas.

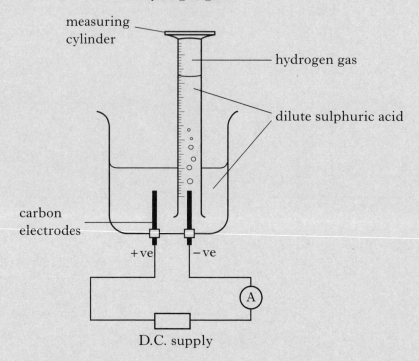

measuring cylinder

hydrogen gas

dilute sulphuric acid

carbon electrodes

+ve   −ve

A

D.C. supply

(a) The measurements recorded by the student were:

Current = 0·5A
Time = 14 minutes
Volume of hydrogen collected = 52 cm^3

Calculate the molar volume of hydrogen gas.

Show your working clearly.

3

(b) What change could be made to the apparatus to reduce a possible significant source of error?

1

[END OF QUESTION PAPER]

(4)

[BLANK PAGE]

ADDITIONAL SPACE FOR ANSWERS

ADDITIONAL GRAPH PAPER FOR QUESTION 3(*a*)

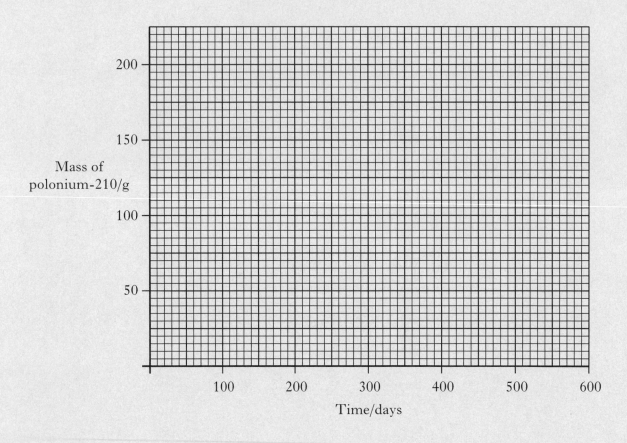

ADDITIONAL GRAPH PAPER FOR QUESTION 11(*a*)

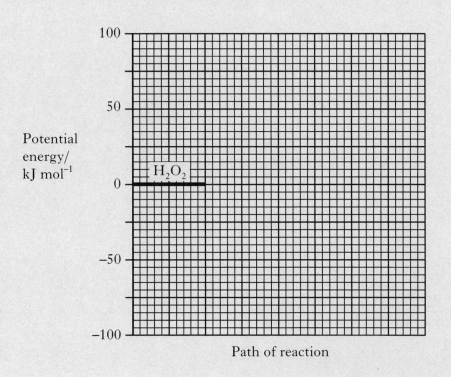